PROSPECTING FOR GOLD

ION IDRIESS

ETT IMPRINT

Exile Bay

This 24ᵗʰ edition published by ETT IMPRINT, Exile Bay 2024
as an Imprint Classic

First published in Australia in 1931 by Angus & Robertson
Revised edition 1931 (twice); Reprinted 1932, 1933, 1934, 1936, 1939,
1944, 1946, 1954, 1962, 1964, 1966, 1968, 1970, 1979, 1982

New edition published by ETT IMPRINT in 1995, reprinted in 2016,
2020, 2022, 2023

ETT IMPRINT
PO Box R1906
Royal Exchange NSW 1225
Australia

ISBN   978-1-923024-61-8   (pbk)
ISBN   978-1-922384-03-4   (ebk)

Cover design by Tom Thompson
Cover : Gold prospectors at Vegetable Creek, New England, NSW

CONTENTS

I	The Likeliest Country To Try	5
II	Prospecting	9
III	Dishing, Banjoing, And Cradling	14
IV	Water Power And Boxing	20
V	Hand Sluicing And More Power	26
VI	Sluicing And Cleaning Up	31
VII	Gold Saving And Dam Building	34
VIII	How To Make Water Work	46
IX	River Work: Osmiridium: Platinum	50
X	Secrets Of Alluvial Gold	55
XI	Dry-Stacking	61
XII	Wet Season Claims—Prospecting For Old River-Beds	66
XIII	Hydraulic Sluicing	71
XIV	Hydraulic Sluicing (Continued)	76
XV	Hydraulic Sluicing (Continued)	82
XVI	Hydraulic Sluicing (Continued)	89
XVII	Elevators	94
XVIII	Dry-Blowing And Nuggets	100
XIX	Prospecting For Reefs	111
XX	Reefing	116
XXI	Erecting A Battery	121
XXII	Amalgamation	127
XXIII	Amalgamation (Continued)	131

XXIV   Battery Work: Complex Ores:

       Cleaning "Silver"   135

XXV   Cyanide   Poisoning   And   Cure:

       Cleaning Up Old Battery Sites   140

XXVI Opal-Mining—Black Opal   143

XXVII Opal-Mining—Light Opal   150

XXVIII You Have A Great Chance   157

XXIX The Cyanide Process   161

XXX   Prospecting For Oil   164

XXXI Your Far Greater Chance   175

       Glossary   179

       Index   183

I

The likeliest country to try

This book is written to help the new hand who ventures into the bush seeking gold. The writer is trying to put into these chapters the practical experience of twenty years. The "towny" prospector, with this book as a guide, will soon master methods of prospecting and the working of his finds. Otherwise, he might well find himself in the position of a man given a job about which he knows absolutely nothing.

The first thing in gold-mining is to start out with the necessary equipment. For the alluvial miner, this is simple. A tent, axe, pick, long and short handled shovels, prospecting dish, cooking utensils, money for "tucker", and a cheerful heart are about all that are necessary. For the prospector, more of course is required. He is the man, the pioneer, who opens up totally unknown country. He must be a good bushman, have had years of experience, have twelve months' supplies of provisions, and pack-horses to carry them. The prospector can well look after himself. But even he is ever anxious to learn; for modern days bring modern methods, and new discoveries in science and industry are constantly bringing hitherto neglected minerals into the commercial market.

Having the equipment, the next question is:

"Where to go?" To gold country. Otherwise, unlike the experienced prospector, you might wander and toil for months in country geologically unsuited for gold. Hence, apply to the Mines Department for advice on this question. Its officers are only too willing to help. They will show you a mineral map of whatever State you are in. On that map are hundreds of areas marked in different colours; and you may choose any gold area you please. So long as you go to a gold-bearing district, you have a chance from the start. Leave the untried country to the experienced man. Your chance there will come later when you have learned how to prospect.

In the older States, New South Wales and Victoria for instance, there are very few areas of country which have not been "gone over;" that is, country over which prospectors have ridden while trying a creek here and there seeking highly payable and easily recoverable gold. But in plenty of these areas gold or gold conditions have been reported, although the country itself has not been extensively worked.

I would advise seekers to choose such an area. Consult the Mines Department for country geologically favourable for the possible recovery of gold. By going to an old field, you of course have the chance of winning a little gold from the start, "tucker money"—that is, you become a fossicker. You are on almost a sure thing so far as the immediate necessaries of life are concerned. But you have far less chance of making a "find" than if you go to proved auriferous country from which the major part of the gold has not been already won.

So take a little more risk and go to auriferous but "new" country. You have the chance not only of making a decent find for yourself, but of doing something far better, of possibly opening up a new field when your country needs one desperately.

Having decided on your locality, the Mines Department will tell you if in doubt how to get there. In the more thickly populated States trains go through practically every district. Go to the town nearest to your district. Then have a chat with the police sergeant. He is generally the clerk to the mining warden and always a mine of information in himself. He will tell you what is doing for fifty miles around. What creeks are being worked where men are "gully raking" in the ranges; the likeliest country to try, etc. He will introduce you to the storekeeper, and tell you exactly where to hire truck or horse and cart or pack-horses to take you and your gear right to the most suitable locality.

A word here before you start work. You already have your tools. It is inadvisable to load up with more. As experience and necessity teach, you will accumulate the few other tools needed. You are mostly quite inexperienced men, seeking the easiest won gold, and yet by the most effective means.

Here let me answer possible questions. In a well-equipped prospector's outfit are always half a dozen picks, several different kinds of shovels, a dolly-pot, magnifying glass, magnet, sharp tomahawk with hammer head, a file, small bellows, half a dozen drills, a hammer, and perhaps a small bottle of "silver" (quicksilver) as well as windlass rope. An occasional prospector may carry a block of charcoal, some borax, platinum wire, acids, and other chemicals. But few men indeed carry these laboratories. The prospector carries all this paraphernalia because he is out after every mineral. Your main object is alluvial gold. You will "pick up" these other tools and their uses as you go along.

Having pitched your camp, take a walk along to any men who may be working in your locality. Be friendly with them, and you will find that bushmen will teach you all they know. Take every chance you have of watching experienced men working. Admit your ignorance. In nine cases out of ten they will talk and explain, and you will learn wonderfully quickly.

So you start your experiences in auriferous country. All around you see mountains of slate or granite, of quartz or ironstone or diorite. A mountain of quartz is unusual. But I have seen hills of quartz, and some mountains upon which quartz was so thickly strewn that for prospecting purposes you and I could class it as a "mountain" of quartz. Get to recognize the ordinary rocks that are associated with "gold country," and in due time they will be like the leaves of a book to you when you go prospecting into untried country "on your own."

Alluvial gold is generally found in watercourses, in rivers, creeks, gullies, ravines. Often in flats. Sometimes deep under basalt or other rock in hidden river-beds of long ago. But those old-time beds take finding and a knowledge of working when found. What will interest you mainly is any watercourse above ground, or any depression in the ground. If gold has once been in the surrounding hills or mountains, by now much of it has been washed down into the depression or watercourse nearest to the source of supply. Understand that that depression is now filled in with stones and earth upon which trees and grass are growing. But if you look closely you will see the hollow, the "depression," in the ground. There may be alluvial wash at the bottom of it.

Therefore, always try the water-courses. In every watercourse, whether it be running river or dry gully, the payable gold will invariably be found in the centre of that course, and right on the very bottom. Should it be in the terraces, or flat, or higher up or down the hill-slope, that is because the old course flowed there centuries ago and has long since been covered up. You will learn later how to locate that hidden course. You will find your first "prospect" under conditions wherein so much Australian gold has been found —in a dry watercourse some distance from a waterhole. By stages you will learn of gold on the tops of hills, on the sides of hills, under hills, under flats, in the "grass roots," in running water-courses and of, what is almost as important, the harnessing of that water to win the gold much faster than picks, shovels, and muscles can win it.

II

Prospecting

The prospecting of ground is of the utmost importance. The results in your dish are what first tell you whether that particular ground is worth working or not. Look at the creek. It is an ordinary dry watercourse; its bedrock or "bottom" is of granite or slate; it is filled with wash and stones of quartz and ironstone. Those are the stones the beginner becomes familiar with first. They are "gold country."

Across your creek runs a "bar," a wall of solid rock. You will see such a bar in almost any creek. But to you it may mean much more. Perhaps it is quite bare rock, with, apparently, as much hope of containing gold as a George Street footpath. Running parallel in that bar are numerous cracks, from the thickness of a knife blade to inches wide. Some cracks are only inches deep, others may be feet. Pick out the gravel and wash-stones jammed by floods deep down in those cracks. If any gold has been washed down that creek, some of it is certain to have lodged in that bar. Grains and specks of it, nicely concentrated, have been driven and pounded with the heavier gravels into the deepest depths of those cracks.

"Crevicing" is a form of gold seeking, often indulged in by old diggers, that invariably yields payable results even on worked out fields—providing, always, some knowing one has not "creviced" before you. Those cracks along the bar are the crevices. The deeper ones you root out with the pick. You scrape out the smaller with a length of hoop-iron with the end bent as a "scraper." For the tiny cracks you use a short piece of fencing wire, the end bent like a hook, the tip flattened. Often when picking the sometimes hardly visible cracks in a slate or granite bar, you find layers of the rock chipping up, as if it had been a huge biscuit, steel hard, full of invisible cracks that break under the pick blows. Good! Keep on chipping; every flake or layer that chips away means the chance of so many more specks of gold wedged down those almost "cemented" cracks. Get every colour of dirt in those crevices: put all in the dish. On some of the edges of the "rotten" or "flaky" stone that your pick has broken off, you will notice a "ribbon" of caked mud or "cement" that was the crack. Wash that stuff off into the dish. Tiny specks of gold may well be wedged into it. If you are trying a new creek, there certainly will be gold in those crevices if gold has come down the creek. No matter how many times a creek has been worked, if the diggers were not "awake" to crevicing there will be gold left in those bars for you. I know men in northern fields who seldom do anything else than "crevicing."

DISHING

When your dish is full, carry it to the nearest water, immerse it, and "puddle" the dirt with your fingers as kids do when making a mud-pie. Squash the harder clods and "dissolve" any lumps of clay.

Then take out the handiest stones, and swirl the dish around with a strong rotary motion, shaking the dish to and fro. Then slightly tip it and dip the "lip" in the water, withdrawing it at such an angle that the water runs off taking with it half an inch depth of the top gravel. Repeat the process all over again. With each washing as you shake the dish the gold sinks to the bottom. Be careful when you have the last few handfuls of heavy sands at the bottom of the dish. Keep washing until there is only a spoonful left; then, with very little water in the dish, give the dirt a little twirl and the gold, if any, will shine at one corner of the sands. The knack in dishing comes to everyone with practice. If you only get a "fly-speck" in the dish, or even no colour at all, try again. Try all along the bar. Whether or not you get results there, you must try the creek proper. If the bar prospects prove that gold has come down the creek, then you must attempt to locate where that gold came from.

Choose the centre of the creek. There, as a rule, the centre is deepest; the water has been dragging the gold into that channel for ages past. With pick and shovel remove whatever depth of sand, gravels, and rocks lie above where you wish to try. Don't waste time trying the surface gravels in a creek. Dig down to solid rock, the "bottom." Gold invariably clings to the bottom. Only bother about the last inch of gravels on the hard bottom; and pay particular attention to any cracks in the bottom. Fill your dish by scraping the bottom. If you take any useless dirt it simply means that you dig it, carry it away, and wash it for nothing. Don't waste time and hard work. Pick the bottom to make sure that you really are on bottom, and pay particular attention to any little depression. Scrape it out; scrape deep where any boulder has lain on the bottom; root out every crack. In those out of the way crevices the gold concentrates. A crevice or a "bump" is a "catch." If you do not scrape and chip the bottom thoroughly you may leave half an ounce of gold in the crevices and get barely a colour in the dish.

Wash your prospect, and if it pans out a "duffer" try a line of prospects, ever working up the centre of the creek. If you are on prospects but not payable prospects, carry on up to the head of the creek until you locate where the payable gold is being shed. It generally comes from up near the heads of the creeks. Remember it comes from somewhere, even if you have not the luck to locate it. Thus you prospect your creek until you prove it a duffer or strike payable ground. Never forget to prospect a bar. You will get, at least, results there if any gold has come down the creek.

Alluvial gold often runs in a "lead," or a "gutter." That is, it may run in a more or less broken "line," perhaps only one foot wide, down the centre of a creek. Ground to either side of it may hold a little gold here and there, but nothing like the payable quantity that is concentrated in a lead. Hence, if you are lucky enough to strike a lead follow it wherever it twists and turns. As to whether you work the ground on either side, that depends on your skill with the prospecting dish. Prospect the ground thoroughly, and if dish prospects point to sufficient gold in the outside ground to pay for the shifting of it, then, of course, work it.

Remember this: in some alluvial ground there may be two or more leads running parallel. To test their existence, cut a trench every thirty feet or less, right across your ground, and dish the bottom of the trench from end to end. If you cut a parallel lead you will thus find it.

In yet other ground, the gold is more widely distributed j or it may have formed in little isolated "pockets;" or be scattered over the bottom as a sower would sow corn. To prove such ground after having located it with the dish, the one method is to "paddock" it. Strip a square of the surface, or in any shape you fancy in a day's work. Next day take up the bottom and dish it. The resulting gold won will tell you what you have made on the labour expended. But always try a number of paddocks before you declare ground a duffer. However, if you happen to be prospecting ground where the gold occurs in "pockets," you may try numerous dishes before locating a decent prospect. Then, when your tail is dragging on the ground, you will suddenly wash a couple of ounces to the dish. You will have struck a pocket of gold in fact.

Dish prospects are rarely consistent, for gold itself is inconsistent in its occurrence. Hence, numerous prospects must be taken before ground can be declared payable or otherwise. Also, ground is "different." What will pay in some country may not pay in a creek only half a mile away. In clayey country, bouldery country, over-burden, gold must be richer than in lightly over-burdened ground with "free" dirt that can be worked easily and quickly. Also, some ground may be close to running water, other ground miles from the nearest still pool. Different methods of treatment must be used with each. Shaft sinking and driving may be necessary to work some ground. It is impossible to give a hard and fast rule as to what prospect of gold is payable and what is not. It all depends on the ground, as to whether you have to shift a lot of boulders before you can get at the bottom wash, whether the bottom is clayey or not, and the distance from water. Experience very soon teaches a man whether he is on payable ground or not. When you "clean up" at the end of the week your gold scales will tell you exactly how much gold you have won. If you haven't got scales, the store-keeper will, quick and lively, tell you. In any case, once you strike colours of gold anywhere, try to follow them up with the dish to their source —to where the gold is being shed. Locate the source of any gold and you have payable ground. It is not always necessary to locate the source either, for a creek may hold a three mile length of payable claims, and yet the actual "source" of that gold never be discovered.

If you do not locate gold in one creek, try all the ravines, creeks, gullies, terraces, within a five mile radius of your camp. Then shift your camp eight miles "farther out," and try every water-course, or what might have been a watercourse, within a five mile radius of your new camp. If you see a long depression, a hollow, in the ground that you think might have been a creek ten thousand years ago, sink a "pot-hole" in the centre of it and try to bottom on an old river-bed. That is how ancient alluvial river-beds are struck. Should you really bottom on such a bed, don't give up if your dishes are "duffers." Search for a lead by putting a cutting right across the bed and dishing the bottom of the cutting. If you fail to locate a lead with your first cutting, try another higher up. In every lead there is a "break": you may have put your cutting right across the break.

Never get discouraged when prospecting likely looking ground. A duffer dish merely means that you have tried in the wrong place. Try a score more dishes: you can wash a hundred a day. On the other hand, if you drop your tail you will only wash a dozen dishes and then hang round the camp all day like a bear with a sore head. Try and try again. If you don't get gold to-day you may tomorrow, and there are plenty of tomorrows. But always try to get your gold in "just another dish." If you finally declare the old bed or the old hill or the creek a duffer, pack up your camp and shift eight miles farther out. There is gold somewhere.

III

Dishing, Banjoing and Cradling

Having located payable ground, you proceed to work it. Strip off the overburden with pick and shovel and throw it aside; but not on ground you will want to work later. Overburden is the surface ground, in fact any ground which carries very little or no gold. You only want the very bottom. Strip for a week, a month. How long depends on whether the storekeeper is pressing for your account. Then pick up the bottom and shovel it into a heap. Throw away all stones: there will be less to carry. If you are in reef or "specimen" country, keep an eye on any iron or quartz stones you pick from the bottom of the wash. There may be odd specimens among those stones. If so, dolly them later and recover the gold. Some forms of ironstone specimens are hard to distinguish: the gold is coated with a film of iron. As on a "specimen field," some stones may carry from a penny-weight to twenty ounces of gold, you will soon learn to cast a practised eye on ironstone and quartz among the wash. "Specimen country" is a term used for mineral country wherein the reefs have shed numerous specimens down into the gullies, creeks, valleys and flats. A specimen is a piece of stone, containing rich mineral, which has broken away from or been shed from a reef. Many alluvial fields carry specimens.

Cart, pack-horse, or wheelbarrow your accumulated wash-dirt to the nearest waterhole. Not being running water the ordinary method of working is by banjo or cradle. A few hardened old-timers prefer to dish their dirt; but the process is very slow.

"Banjoing" is back-breaking work. Still, in portions of Australia, particularly the far north, some men become remarkably proficient. A banjo is simply an open box, about four feet long. The "head" of the box may be two feet high, with the sides sloping to six inches. The width is two feet at the head, tapering to eighteen inches at the end. This narrowing of the width is important. The bottom is covered with bagging. The tail of the box is open; but there is inserted a two-inch "ripple"—two pieces of board fastened across the tail to hold back the sands. The banjo is placed, in a slightly sloping position, right against the edge of the waterhole. The digger throws a few shovelfuls of dirt well up into the head of the box. Then he steps into the water, grabs his prospecting dish, and throws a dishful of water into the tail of the box so that it rolls up to the dirt at the head and, partly dissolving it, comes back like a receding wave. This is met by another dish of water and another and another until the dirt is reduced to the level of the ripple. There is then about an inch depth of heavy sands in the banjo. This is carefully scraped to the head of the banjo, a few more shovelfuls put in, and the procedure repeated. When all the dirt has been put through, the concentrates are put into the dish and washed.

There is a distinct knack in banjoing only acquired by practice. The new chum would inevitably lose gold. The idea is to keep the water striking the tail of the banjo so that, though the sludge runs out, the oncoming water carries the heavier concentrates containing the gold back to the head of the box. The water can be used over and over again. When the hole is filled up with tailings they are shovelled out and the water re-used until it is almost sludge. Banjoing is backbreaking work while it lasts.

"Cradling" is a time-honoured process of gold recovery. Providing the cradle be faithfully made there is little chance of losing gold. A cradle is an oblong box open at one end. It has a movable hopper, several slides fitted with ripples, and is fitted with rockers upon which it rocks just like a child's cradle. It is simplicity itself to make and operate.

When making the cradle use as light wood as possible, for ease in carrying about. A usual measurement is forty inches long by twenty inches wide, and two feet high at the back end. The sides slope down to the "tail" of the box, out of which the tailings flow. The hopper is movable: make it to fit into the top of the cradle. Remembering that wood swells when wet, do not make it too tight. The hopper, usually, is a wooden frame twenty inches square and six inches deep, the bottom of which is sheet iron punched with half-inch holes. It is just a sieve into which the dirt is put.

So you have your hopper resting on top of an open box.

Now, some men make a cradle with only one slide. In such a case the cradle box has only three sides. Many men prefer a deeper box, with a door or bagging to cover the open side. Into this they fit three slides. You may open the "door," to pull the slides out, or slip them in. Such a cradle would perhaps be better suited to the new chum. There is less chance of losing gold.

A slide is simply a flat board, crossed with wooden ripples. This, at a steeply sloping angle, fits into slits on the inside of the box. Between the lower edge of each slide and the side of the box a space is left to allow the wash to fall on to the top of the slide below (see sketch). It is a good idea to line the slides with canvas or bag: it helps to hold fine gold. Across each slide, at a distance of say two inches apart, is a ripple. This is simply a stick ¼-inch high. These ripples help to hold the gold. Each ripple can be tacked down through the canvas on to the slide. Our box has two of these slides.

Now get the idea. The hopper fits down into the top of the box. The dirt is washed through the hopper and falls on to the first slide along which it runs to fall on the second slide, and down it on to the third slide (if three are used), which carries the water and earth to the rear and bottom of the box.

Thus the wash-dirt, on its zigzag way, has to travel quite a little distance, and each ripple it traverses stops some of the gold. At the bottom of the box is bagging or a piece of blanket, with several ripples (inch high this time) which stop the heavy sands and fine gold. The wash-dirt and water escape through the opening at the bottom (the "tail") of the box. Projecting from the bottom is generally a "lip"—merely the boarding carried out a further two feet so as to save very fine gold. The depth of the box depends on individual liking and the number of slides a man wishes to use. The slides are held in place by slats.

The rockers of course fit on the bottom of the box. A good plan is to fit the centre of each rocker with a long iron pin, projecting downward, to fit into a corresponding hole in a wooden stand. This stand (or bed-piece) is simply four planks. The cradle rocks very freely on such a frame, more so, you can understand, than if it were rocked on the uneven earth.

When you "set" your cradle for work, set it on a slight incline. This incline really means "fall," a term you must quickly become familiar with. If the back of your cradle is raised say one inch higher than the tail, then the tailings will run out easier and quicker than if you set the cradle level on the

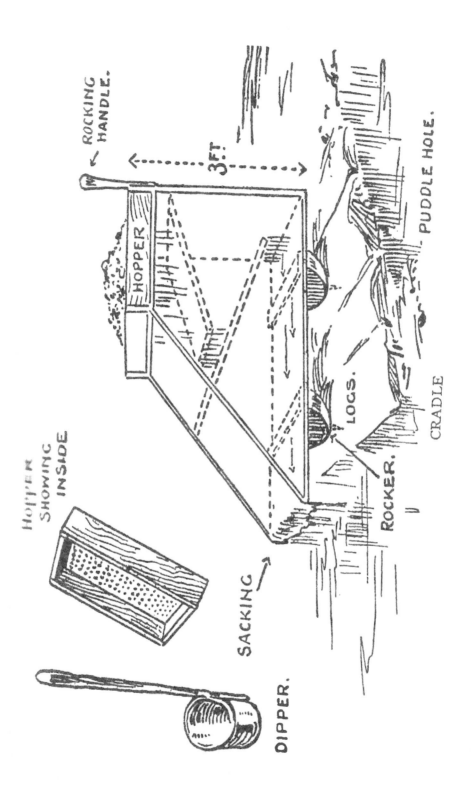

ROCKING HANDLE.

3 FT.

HOPPER

PUDDLE HOLE.

HOPPER SHOWING INSIDE

LOGS.

CRADLE

ROCKER.

SACKING

DIPPER.

ground. Set the cradle to suit the dirt you are putting through. Heavy sands for instance require more "fall" than ordinary surface ground. But be careful. If you are working ground in which the gold is light, flaky, or impure, you are very likely to lose gold if you set your cradle with too much fall. Gold which is flaky, or contains silver or other impurities, is sometimes lighter even than heavy sands. Hence, with too much fall such gold is liable to escape from the cradle faster than the heavy sands.

No matter what class of gold you are working, when you have been cradling for two hours try a dishful of your tailings. If gold shows in the dish you certainly have too much fall in your cradle.

The remaining apparatus of a cradle is also simple. It is a stick, to the end of which is nailed an empty fruit or treacle tin. This is your "dipper." Put several shovelfuls of wash on the hopper, rock the handle with one hand, reach to the waterhole with the dipper, and pour water on the hopper while rocking. As the dirt is washed through the hopper, put more on, etc. The hopper soon collects stones. When this happens wash the hopper clean, quickly examine the stones in case of a small specimen; then lift out the hopper, throw the stones aside, replace the hopper, and carry on.

If you are working good ground in coarse gold country, be careful that you do not throw away any "weight" pieces of gold when you throw the stones from the hopper. Every hour, or less if you are on good ground, look at your first slide when you lift the hopper off. If gold is showing, clean the slide.

To clean up, which you do if the gold is showing at all freely among the ripples, take off the hopper, lift out the slides and wash them into the dish. Wash the dish of concentrates. Then run water into the box and wash the sands in the bottom into the dish. Wash this dish of "fines" and you have cleaned up.

In working a cradle, the fine sands at the bottom of the box sometimes cake hard as cement. If so, stir the sand occasionally; otherwise fine gold is liable to be washed over the hard surface. Should the wash-dirt be clayey, it must be puddled before putting through the cradle. Clay rolls into balls, collects particles of gold, and rolls away with it. So the clay must be dissolved— so far as water will "dissolve" it. "Free dirt" does not require puddling.

To puddle:—Chop a hollow log into a trough and board up both ends. In one of the end boards bore an inch hole level with the centre of the trough, and plug it with wood. Partly fill the trough with wash-dirt, then fill with water. Stir the mess vigorously with the shovel. As the water thickens, pull out the plug and let the slime run away. Insert the plug, fill with water again, and stir until all the clay has been washed from the dirt. Then put the dirt through the cradle.

Puddling is hard work, but you must free the dirt of clay. A helpful plan is to let the dirt soak overnight. If you are near running water, and have the water running into the trough, a lot of labour is saved. A tiptop idea for "dissolving" thick clay or "pug" is to throw a few shovelfuls of coarse sand or gravel into the trough, then stir. The sharp grain sands cut the clay and materially hasten the disintegrating process.

Wash the clay from the wash-stones before throwing them away. Clay will "pick up" gold wherever it touches it. As a layer of clay is frequently on bottom, it may carry much of the gold; so all the bottom clay must be thoroughly broken up in any method of treatment for recovering the gold which it may contain.

IV

Water power and boxing

Now for a much faster method of gold working, "boxing." And right here I strongly advise the gold seeker to always remember that water works. Which means that a man can make very poor ground pay, if he has the water and understands how to work that water.

We will take the case of an alluvial creek that is a chain of waterholes, with the barest trickle of running water in some part of the creek.' Perhaps long areas of the creek appear quite dry sand. But water is really slowly draining underneath. Farther up the creek, over a rock bar, is a wee dribble of water, not worth noticing. That water really means power. There are countless such creeks in Australia, and many of them hold gold in greater or lesser degree.

In prospecting, you find that the bottom of this creek holds gold, but in poor quantity. Even your inexperience tells you that you could not dig and shift the overburden, scrape up the bottom, put it through the cradle, and make it pay. With a quicker method you might: you would be very willing to give it a try anyway. Well, make a sluice-box. If you make it of heavy boards serve you right. It is you who will have to carry it from place to place. A cradle is simple enough to make; a sluice-box simpler. Men who understand thoroughly the saving of fine gold, won't have anything to do with a box over five feet long—a little bit of a thing they can pick up and sling over the shoulder and carry over boulders to a new "possy" half a mile away.

But the new chum had better make his box ten feet in length. He and his mate can carry it anywhere within reason. It is a safe type of box if you are settled in a claim with at least months of work ahead; particularly if you are working a bank of wash or gravels in such quantity that you wish to wheelbarrow into the box. I will describe a much lighter type of box later on. If possible, make the bottom of one board two feet wide at the top end tapering to eighteen inches at the extremity or "tail." Failing one board for the bottom, use two: see that the join is perfectly even and tight. Each side of your box will be a board ten feet long, the "head" end of it two feet wide, tapering to one foot. Tightly nail your sides to the bottom. Then nail in the "head," a board two feet high. The "tail" of the box is open. On each inner side of the end, nail a narrow slat. These slats hold the ripple, or ripples, in place. Each ripple is a light board, one inch wide, a shade less in length than the width of the end of the box. Thus, when placed in position, one upon the other at the end of the box, each ripple raises the level of the water or sand in the box, one inch. At the head of the box, on the side boards, nail two little slats about eight inches long, running back towards the head of the box (see sketch). On these slats rests a flat board—a splash board. Its object is to confine the water evenly so that it runs with force straight down the head of the box. This board is not absolutely necessary, but it ensures added quickness and efficiency in working. In gold-digging always remember to make your head save your hands. The fossicker who mines with both recovers far more gold than the man who mines with his hands alone. Always seek for efficiency and quick methods in working.

Now as to the vexed question of saving the gold. The expert does not worry about it nearly so much as the new chum. Providing any apparatus is set at the right angle, and the ordinary proved methods are employed for the saving, there is really little chance of losing gold. In widely scattered parts of Australia where the sluice-box and sluicing methods are employed, particularly in northern Australia, in Papua, and in the Mandated Territory of New Guinea, the sluicers mainly rely on lining the bottom of the box with a blanket, "paving" the last two feet of the box with stones, and on the bottom ripple, to save their gold. For fine gold of course more care has to be taken. Methods of saving fine gold will be discussed in a later chapter. I have always found that the forking stones in the head of the box save by far the largest proportion of the gold.

Now for your water-supply. Find where the water trickles down the creek, as near where you work as possible. Choose a spot too where you may see the water flowing over a bar. A bar as you know is solid rock, rising up right across the creek, perhaps damming it back into a waterhole. If you have the

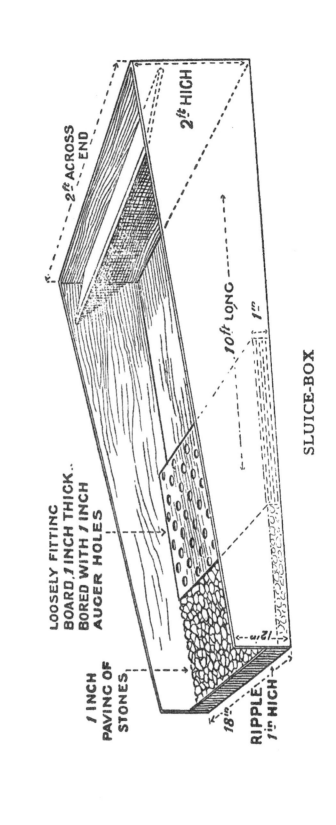

2ft ACROSS END

2ft HIGH

10ft LONG

1in

LOOSELY FITTING BOARD, 1 INCH THICK.. BORED WITH 1 INCH AUGER HOLES

1 INCH PAVING OF STONES

12in

18in

RIPPLE 1in HIGH

SLUICE-BOX

water running over a bar you have all the water: it is running over bare rock and not away through sand below.

Raise the level of that water. Throw a dam, say two feet high, on the bar, right across the creek. A couple of days work will do it; a few logs, plenty of bushes, grass for binding, and loam well stamped down. First, in the centre of the dam, at bottom level, put in a small hollow log plugged with a bag.

Next, cut a light race from the dam outlet to run along the creek bank to your box. Thus you will have running water within reach of your shovel blade at your command. With the spout of the dam plugged the water will be accumulating while you are working or sleeping. The smaller the catchment area for your dam, the higher, of course, you must build your retaining wall.

Next "set" your box. This is important, but easily done. Lay the box at a slant of say one inch in twelve feet. Put one ripple in the tail of the box. This raises the water in the box. Now raise or lower the head of the box so that the water coming in over the head shoots straight down the box before it begins to deepen, due to the ripple raising the level. When eighteen inches of the bottom at the head of the box appears bare, that is, has a film of swiftly moving water scooting down the bottom before the water deepens, then the box is set right. Turn off your water (just throw a filled sand-bag in the race at the head of the box), take out the ripple, and the water leaves the box. Shovel earth underneath it so that the box sets down on a firm bed. Next put in your strip of blanket right along the bottom, of the box. Some men prefer to leave the head bare; but please yourself. I myself leave two feet of the head of a box bare, otherwise when forking the prongs of the fork are very liable to catch in the blanket. A wooden slat here and there helps to keep the blanket in position. Now put in one ripple at the tail of the box: put in two if you are scared of losing gold. Then from the bottom ripple, to say, three feet up "pave" the box with small stones by packing rows of stones across the box. The idea is to catch among the stones any fine gold coming down the box. Your box is now ready.

Get to work on your ground. Strip it and get the bottom out. Place the box so that you can drop the dirt straight into the box head. Some men shovel their ground four times, thus reducing their gain in gold by nearly a fourth. In ground that is muddy, or under or partly under water, you must be especially careful in cleaning up the bottom. Scrape out every spoonful of mud from crevice or crack. Leave the rough uneven bottom of the creek as bare and clean as a woman's kitchen floor. Only so will you get all the gold. That is the way the Chinaman works. No man ever yet found gold after Chinamen have worked a creek, so they say.

Now partly pull the plug from your dam, letting only sufficient water run to work the box. Walk back to your box and regulate the exact flow by means of the sand-bag at its head. Allow just enough water through the box to wash away the gravels as fast as you put in the wash-dirt and fork the stones. One hour's experience will teach you. Always regulate your water by means of the dam plug so that none is wasted.

Now shovel some dirt well up into the head of the box. The water splashes on it and immediately the sands begin to flow down and out at the tail. The stones stay at the head of the box. Don't be in a rush to fork out the stones: they help to hold the gold at the head of the box. As the stones accumulate fork them out by means of the sluice fork, a hay fork, as it were, with straighter prongs. The gravels fall away through the prongs back into the box as you throw the forkful of stones aside. How many times easier and faster than the laborious old cradle hopper! And, if there is a specimen stone among the forkings you will see the glint of gold from the water. Drop your fork, and shovel in more dirt.

Do you understand that with a sluice-box you can put through the dirt as fast as you can shovel it in and fork out the stones? You will put through twenty times as much dirt in a day as you could with a cradle. Consequently, much poorer ground than a cradle could treat would pay handsomely with a sluice box. You can work as long as your dam lasts. It is a poor dam indeed that won't give an hour or two's run in the morning, and during that time you can put through all the ground you dug the day before. With a decent dam, countless creeks will supply sufficient water for a six hours run.

Most of your gold, certainly all the coarse, will be at the head of the box. At smoke-oh, let the box "run down." Do this by turning aside some of the water from the head of the box, allowing the lessened stream to gently but partially clear the sands and rubble from the head. If you see gold sparkling, clean up the head of the box only. With the shovel, or far better with a flat piece of iron about half the size of the shovel blade, keep throwing the sands, starting from the top of the paving, to the head of the box. The water all the time is washing the sands away until concentrates only are left. Turn aside all the water, lift the concentrates into the dish, and wash them for the gold.

To clean the box at knock-off time, let the box "run down;" at the same time keep throwing the sands to the head of the box until their bulk is reduced. Then loosen the paving stones; throw them to the head of the box; fork them out, and again reduce the box, this time to concentrates. Lift these out into the dish. Then turn off the water; carefully up-end the blanket in the box; and let the water flow very gently and carefully as you wash the blanket still in the box. Next put the dish under the tail of the box, let the water flow gently down the box, and with your hands or a brush of grass sweep the "fines" down the box into the dish. Wash the dish and you have your gold.

The type of box just described is used very generally on claims that will be payable for years, and on ground that has been proved will provide steady work for at least months. Once the box is set, it may remain for weeks, perhaps months without having to be moved. The depth of the box is such that a small wheelbarrow of dirt can be tipped into it at a time. That is a method quite often employed on northern tin fields, one man picking out the dirt, another shovelling it into the "barrow" and harrowing it down to the box, a third man remaining in the box and putting the dirt through. The only difference between alluvial tin and gold methods of box working is in the ripples.

However, the box just described is weighty and awkward to carry for any distance. Also, numbers of men discard the paving of stones. Though the long box is ideal on a definitely proved claim, in a later chapter I will describe a light box which one man can make, work, and carry for miles if he is shifting from creek to creek.

V

Hand sluicing and more powers

As boxing is faster than cradling, so is hand sluicing than boxing. It is very poor ground indeed that won't pay to hand sluice. The one imperative necessity is running water to sluice with. Even with a little running water, you can force Nature's hand. Should a stream bed be near you which carries only a gentle trickle, you can build a dam sufficiently large to provide water to hand sluice with for four hours per day. With four hours sluicing water you can shift a surprising quantity of ground. In hand sluicing you almost do away with the heaviest labour in mining—shovelling. The water does that for you.

We will now suppose that you are prospecting in mountainous country. You have struck a running stream which carries values. A few colours of shorty gold seem to be scattered here and there all along and over the bottom of the creek. But in lots of dishes you don't get a trace. It looks a poor prospect. You are dubious as you "sum up" that stream. You estimate how much ground you can put through a box, and you don't think this ground will pay for the quantity which you can put through. However, there is constantly running water here, so hand sluice the creek and thus put through twenty times the amount of ground in a day that you could with a box. You will most likely find, then, that this poorer ground will pay handsomely. If you have constantly running water, it means a very great deal to you; it means free, tireless labour.

There must be "fall" for hand sluicing. Every creek has fall. Occasional creeks, however, may hardly have a fall of two feet in two miles. Such a creek cannot be sluiced (without elevating machinery) because there is no fall to take away the "tailings."

Any mountain stream has abundance of fall. Observe closely, and such a stream will appear to run in sections; the water running for a hundred yards, say, to fall over a ledge for a foot or two, then carry on to another fall. Start your tail-race at such a fall at the bottom end of your claim. This tail-race is to carry away all your tailings. As you work up your claim it is to hold your concentrates and gold.

Now, if a sluice head or two of water is running down the centre of the creek (and so down the centre of your claim if that is in the heart of the creek) all is plain sailing. Don't worry about the quantity of water in a sluice head. Roughly speaking, it is sufficient for one man to comfortably hand sluice with. It can be made to do two men as well as one. But if there is a large volume of water running down the creek then you must turn the surplus water off.

Glance up the creek. Probably at the head of your claim, or higher up, is a ledge over which the water is falling. There is the key where you can turn the water away to one side or the other of your claim.

But suppose the creek is flat for a considerable distance above you. Then above the top of your claim you must throw a few logs with some bushes and earth, build a dam in fact, sufficient to raise the level of the water a foot or more as required.

You thus do what nature does with a ledge.

From the ledge or dam cut a race out on to either bank (if the bank is not too high) and run this race right down the bank along the side of the ground you are going to work and back into the creek below your tail-race. Turn the excess water into this race. Thus you "dry" the creek sufficiently to work it. Should rocks or any other physical obstacle prevent you running the water from the ledge into your excess water race, just flume it across into the race with a few lengths of fluming: bark troughs are the handy thing. Use your head in hand sluicing. A strip of bark fluming here and there will often save you hours, perhaps days, of labour in cutting a race among boulders or over rock.

If the bank is too high above the level of the water, or if you are working in a gorge, then cut a race from the nearest fall above and down along the outside edge of your ground. Thus you turn off the water though not so effectually. When you have worked out the centre and one side of your ground, turn that water on to the worked ground, to enable you to work the remainder of your ground—that upon which you had turned the excess water.

After you have turned away excess water from interfering with your work, train your working sluice head right down the centre of the claim. It will run centre naturally if your claim is in the bed of a creek. Now, start with the pick at the lower end of your tail-race, and pick-up the ground right along the centre, forming a race two feet wide and the depth of the overburden. Leave about six inches depth of the wash that rests upon the hard rock bottom.

You pick in the running water. The water takes the loosened gravels and many of the smaller stones past you away down the race. Take the "forkings" out with the sluice fork, throwing them on ground which you know is too poor to work.

It is pleasant, quick, and easy work, interesting and just hard enough to keep you in Sandow condition. Always use your head and ways will "come" to you of making the water do work you never dreamed it would. Remember, the more work the water does the more ground it is putting through, and correspondingly greater will be your winning of gold.

The ground you are now putting through is overburden of shingles and gravels, and will rarely carry any gold at all. Your object is to rush it through as quickly as possible. It is "overburden." Make your water rush it away. If there really are a few grains of gold in it they will accumulate in the race. Don't worry about the gold at this stage.

When you have sluiced your race thus for a length of say fifty feet, go back to where you started and pick-up the bottom. Turn off the flow of water just a little. Don't rush this bottom away; use just sufficient water to ensure the tailings being washed away as you pick the ground. If you are so afraid of losing gold that you slow down the water too much, then the tailings accumulate in the race and you defeat your object. Any gold will be held back by the stones in the race. Further, when gold touches actual hard bottom, it clings.

If you find a layer of soft slate rock or granite caked on top of the hard bottom, sink your pick into it and loosen it all up. Work right down on to the hard bottom. Auriferous slates and granites are often decomposed for a few inches in depth. Gold will be right down in this soft stone; so work down until you feel the solid bottom under the pick.

When for the second time you have worked to the end of the race, turn the force of water off a little more. You must reduce this strip of race and clean up. You are doing only preparatory work, remember. Start from the bottom end of the race and work right up it with the shovel, pressing the blade and scraping it along the hard bottom, stirring up the dirt and lifting it to drop it back flat into the race again. As you are stirring the gravels you are actually sinking the gold right to the bottom. You are doing the rocking of a cradle. You may be the same man who rocked the cradle, but you are now putting through many times more ground.

If there is any clay on the bottom, much of it has dissolved by previous action of the pick, water, and sands. Dissolve the remainder by movements of the shovel, helped by friction of small stones and the cutting action of water and sands. Leave only sufficient stones in the race to help save the gold. If there is a layer of "puggy" clay resting on the bottom of your claim, then you will be unfortunate. It means extra work.

Puggy clay is unusual. "Puggy" ground often breaks up under the pick to form into sticky clay balls exceptionally awkward to disintegrate. These roll away down the race, collecting gold as they go when the race begins to get "bare." You must break up all these balls. If they are escaping down the race, turn the water off to just that strength at which you can hold them. Constantly stirring the bottom with the shovel will help the cutting action of the sands to quickly break up the clays.

Thus you reduce your race. You are putting no more dirt in, so that soon the bare bottom begins to show up in patches. Fork out stones here and there up along the race. The remaining sands quickly dribble away. You may see a speck or two of gold showing here and there, caught in a bare patch of the race. If you do, and the specks are of any size, always pick them out, and drop them into a handy tin. They may be quite safe in the race, but once in the tin you know they are yours.

When the race is reduced to this stage, experienced men quickly shovel the dirt up towards the head of the race, throw out all the stones, and reduce the remnant to concentrates of heavy black iron-sands and gold. These they dish or box, according to the expertness of the worker. Some men can "reduce" their race to such an extent that there are left only a few dishes of concentrates to "dish."

But the inexperienced worker had better adopt another policy. It is very quick; it will save him much time and labour; and he will not stand the chance of losing gold. Once a race is well reduced it needs experience to save all the gold.

When you have got your race reduced so that it is bare in places with only inch-deep heaps of sands and concentrates elsewhere up and down the race, turn the water off completely, and shovel the remaining dirt in the race into a heap. Then box it. That is all there is to it. But do the job properly. Otherwise you will do slower work and may well leave an ounce or two of gold in the race.

First, set your sluice-box at the end of your race. Then shovel the concentrates out of the race into dishes and empty the dishes on to the tent fly or sheets of bark spread handily beside the box. Then start at the very head of the race and scrape it right down, first with the shovel, after with your hoop-iron scraper. Scrape out cracks, crevices, depressions, every tiny cubby hole where a grain of gold may hide. As you fill the dish with scrapings, carry it to the heap down by the box. When two men are working a claim, one will generally stay in the race reducing it and "working" the heavier sands and concentrates down towards the box, while his mate stands by the box shovelling the sands, as they come down, back up to the head of the box and thus saving the lighter gold.

Finally, you think you have the race as bare as a kitchen floor. Not so. Turn on a little water. Make a broom of a handful of coarse grass stalks or suitable twigs and "follow" the water right down the race, actually sweeping the race bare. It will surprise you the number of colours of gold that will show up. You must clean up the last colour of gold. It takes very little gold to weigh an ounce. And an ounce of gold may be worth £4. If from carelessness or inexperience you leave a few ounces of gold in a long race, you will find your claim won't pay.

Lots of men turn themselves into bullocks, working long strenuous hours to put through big quantities of ground. But in the cleaning up they are often very careless and leave appreciable quantities of gold behind them. When you have got your race bare as a newly polished linoleum, then box the heap of heavy sands, and dish the resultant concentrates.

VI

Sluicing and cleaning up

You have now started to open up your claim. Deepen the race one foot. It must be deeper than the bottom of the surrounding ground. Into this race you must sluice all your ground. So pick the race up. Even though the bottom be flint hard (which is not usual) you must deepen it. Remember to follow up the centre of the creek. This area is slightly deeper than the surrounding bed and with a little picking gives you a natural race. The bedrock you remove in doing this will, of course, hold no gold.

Now run your race up a further fifty feet, or right up through the centre of your claim to its limit if you wish. The deeper race behind, you can partly pave with stones. These hold the gold. Sluice everything into this race. Remember when cutting it to always keep your "fall." The race must be sloping, just like the "set" of your sluice-box. The slope sends the water rushing through the race to carry the tailings away. Otherwise the tailings would bank up and you could not hand sluice. That would bring you right back to the box method of working. If there is too much fall in your race, work it in a series of ledges, or "drops."

You are now going to work your claim out in a "face," for by prospecting you have found that the gold "averages" (is fairly evenly distributed over the bottom). Hence you work in a face, taking everything before you. Working ground in a face means that you miss nothing. Chinamen diggers are firm believers in that method.

From your water-supply, bring a light race down on the extreme edge of your ground, away from the gold-bearing wash. If you are working in a creek-bed you can "spit" this race out with a shovel very quickly. It will run parallel with your main race. Now, beginning at the last strip of ground on the lower end of your claim, "spit" a guiding race straight into your tail-race, from the race you have just dug. Parallel with this, bring in another light race, followed by a series of such races, about three feet apart, so as to "grid-iron" the first "paddock" you intend sluicing out. The accompanying sketch will make plain this very simple procedure.

If the physical features of the ground make it possible to utilize the over-flow race by turning it into the side races, then so much the easier for you. Of course, only in heavily flowing creeks is this turning of the water needed.

Now run your water into the first side race and work out that strip, sluic-ing it out as you did the first start at the tail-race. Leave about six inches of wash on the bottom; unless you prefer to work the ground out strip by strip as you go. Most men prefer to work the bottom separately. By this method the gold is rarely lost: the golden wash is not mixed with the bulkier overburden that you are trying to dispose of on the "rush" principle. Then turn the water into the next side race and sluice out that strip. Carry on so. That is how a "paddock" is sluiced out. You can work at it a week if you like, or a month. The first paddock is generally small, for a spare piece of ground is wanted on which to deposit the forking stones.

Having "stripped" your paddock let the race run down to a considerable extent, giving it a stir with the shovel to settle any gold. You are bound to have touched bottom here and there in the paddock. Bottom is generally all little rises and "bumps," so that some gold must have been sluiced down into your tail-race with the overburden.

Now turn the water back into the first side race you started. Sluice up the bottom strip by strip exactly as you sluiced up the bottom of your tail-race. All the bottom of the paddock as it is sluiced, drops down into your main race. When you have sluiced your last side race, the result is a bare paddock, perhaps thirty feet long by twenty feet wide. Keep your water now running slowly, for you must clean the bottom of that paddock as clean as a new pin. Don't let any sand-filled crack escape you. Any cement-like patch of wash, any areas of "broken" or "rotten" bottom, break up with the pick and sluice away into the tail-race.

If you are on gold at all, you will see it in this paddock. As you are on the hard bottom washing down each side race you should see the gold accumu-lating. If so, and it appears in any quantity, work the concentrates up with the shovel and lift the richest of them into the dish as they appear. While cleaning the paddock bare, you will see most of the gold. A very little handling with the shovel, then, will reduce the sand to rich concentrates. Just lift it aside and later dish it. Many diggers repeatedly work this way when they are cleaning down a paddock. Thus they get 75 per cent of their gold without letting it go into the main race at all. Don't waste time, however, if you only see an odd speck now and again.

When the first paddock is bare, you have room for forkings, roots, logs, and such-like refuse. Then work out another paddock; and so on right up one side of your claim. Naturally, you deepen your main race as you work along. Clean up your main race occasionally—once every week, or fortnight, or month. The longer the interval the better, unless you are on rich gold. To clean up an ordinary tail-race takes a couple of days. So save time by cleaning up the main race nearer once a month.

When one side of your claim is worked out you switch the water across on to the other side and work similarly. If you have worked with ordinary care as regards the bottom, and used your head in the bringing on of races, you will work out that claim in a face and get every ounce of gold in an amazingly short time.

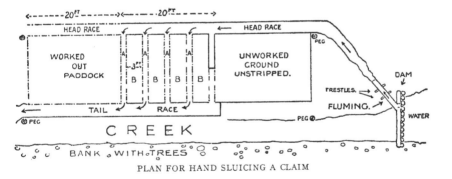

PLAN FOR HAND SLUICING A CLAIM

VII

Gold Saving and Dam Building

If you have mastered the preceding chapters, you know quite a lot about boxing and hand sluicing, the two main methods of "open" working for alluvial gold. Remember to apply your "water knowledge," whenever possible, if you happen to work at other forms of alluvial—sinking or tunnelling for an old river-bed. Cart your wash to the nearest running water and put it through a box, not a cradle or dish. Use your water knowledge even though not actually working sluicing ground.

Now for a few hints on boxing and hand sluicing. The physical conditions of different claims vary. For instance, you can box in a running stream under conditions where it would not be advantageous to hand sluice your whole claim in a face. You have prospected the stream and located a payable claim, but the ground is only payable in small patches. To lower the level of the water, to shift boulders, to shoot a bar, or to carry out other work which you see would be necessary before you could hand sluice, would take up more time, you estimate, than to carry a box from patch to patch of the payable ground and simply box it. Well then box it. In this case the slower method will be the faster. You can box the payable patches and leave the rest.

Now to avoid being puzzled when you hear discussions on various methods of gold saving. A general method of saving gold in a box has been described in chapter IV.

Another but less popular way is to have two two-inch thick boards which fit easily into the bottom of the box. Close-spaced holes are bored in these boards with an inch auger. The idea is to let the water and sands rush over the boards while the gold collects in the holes.

Another form is a "false bottom." This may be a sheet of iron, punched with holes and having the edges turned down an inch all round, to fit in the bottom of the box. The turned down edges raise the false bottom one inch above the bottom of the box. The gold works through the holes and is saved in the sands below the false bottom.

Another form of false bottom is a framework of inch wide sticks, the framework to fit loosely into the bottom of the box. Make the frame-work half the length of the box if you wish to try it.

The illustration explains the idea:

The heavier gravels with the gold sink down between the sticks and come to rest on the box bottom. Another form of ripple sometimes used is the "zigzag." This is a flat board which fits snugly down into the box. Inch thick cleats at varying angles are nailed on to the board so:

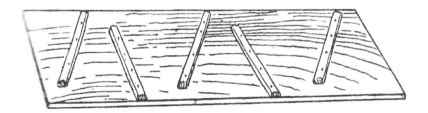

The idea is to force the heavier sands to make a zig-zag course down the box, the gold being blocked by the cross pieces.

"Pin head" gold, and finer, is harder to save. In tropical parts of Australia, in Papua, and the Mandated Territory of New Guinea, a favourite saving device for either coarse or fine gold is basket-work. A wooden frame is made to fit loosely into the box. Across this frame strips of lawyer cane (the schoolteacher's cane split in two) are interlaced into a simple basket-work. The gold is caught among the many interstices of this basket-work. Any that falls or is washed through lodges in the bottom of the box. For very fine gold the box should be long and the flow of water just sufficient to break up and wash away the loam and gravels.

Blanket or ordinary bagging is invariably "blanketed" down the box. Part of the box will, possibly, be carefully paved, another length be under basket-work of cane or pliable sticks, and the last two or three feet covered by "matting." The matting is made of handfuls of stalks or coarse grass, coco-nut husk, fibre bark teased out —anything naturally handy that one's own sense tells one will make a "tricky catch" for fine gold.

In cleaning up fine gold, be extra careful. Wash thoroughly and carefully in the box itself whatever type of saving device you use. If you use matting of any description, wash and shake it well within the box; then lay it aside in a tub or trough or on a sheet of bark. If you are working rich fine gold, remember there still must be gold in that matting. When the matting is wearing out, it may pay you to dry it, burn it, and wash the ashes.

There is invariably a large quantity of heavy black sand with fine gold. This has to be very carefully dished, washing it into another dish. When reduced as clean as possible, dry it. If your concentrates are very rich and in quantity, and you still feel inexperienced, it may well pay you to send away the concentrates and sell them by assay.

However, if you wish to clean and weigh your own gold, here are methods: In small quantities, place the concentrates on a sheet of paper. Gently shake the paper until the concentrates spread out. Then puff gently with the mouth. You will soon gauge your breath to blow away nearly all the sand in this way. Then run a magnet through and through the remainder. Most of the iron grains will cling to the magnet. Brush them off and run through again.

Another way of collecting extra fine gold is with quicksilver (mercury). Put half a spoonful in the dish with your concentrates and shake it until the gold unites with the quicksilver and forms an amalgam. I have seen men "washing" the mercury into the sands with their finger-tips. However, quicksilver is said to penetrate the human fingers and rot the bones and finger-nails. I can't say how true that is. Certainly, the men I know who practise this method have their fingers intact. Perhaps this is because gold so fine as to be worth recovering with mercury, is not often found in quantity. When gold and quicksilver is thus united it is called amalgam.

A simple way of separating the gold from the "silver" is to tip it into a piece of "shammy" leather, or double folded calico like a handkerchief, and screw it round and round very tightly. The silver is squeezed through the calico in little beads and falling back into the dish, is ready for re-use. The gold remains in the calico as a little hard ball. However, you are not likely to meet with gold as fine as that. If you do, you know now how to treat it. A comical but effective method of separating an amalgam bead is to cut a potato in halves, gouge out the centre to the shape of the amalgam, put it in, then put over it the other half of the potato. Twist a piece of wire round the spud then bury it in the hot ashes.

After it has baked a while, open up the spud and there will be a little ball of pure gold shining at you. The "silver" has gone. But crush the potato in your hand, then wash it in the dish and innumerable little beads of silver will come rolling out of the broken potato all ready for you to use again.

Should you, by any chance, come on payable beach sands, I advise you to let the Mines Department know straight away. The Department of Mines, New South Wales, suggests the following method for treating auriferous beach sands: The sand is beaten, screened through a quarter-inch screen, and then fed into a perforated zinc-lined hopper from which it is washed down a table about fourteen feet long and fixed at an angle of thirteen degrees. The table is lined with carpet on which the concentrates of gold and platinum collect. From time to time the concentrates are washed from the carpet, treated with a solution of washing soda and caustic soda, and then run slowly down the table now covered with amalgamated copper plates. The use of the cyanide process has been suggested.

BOXING IN A FLAT CREEK

The dam here is to raise the level of the water so that it will flow into the box.

Along the Australian, and particularly the New Zealand, coast, black sands on the sea beach have been very rich with "mustard" gold. But that is a phase of mining not often met with.

A word now about dams. Choose your location carefully and save yourself much time and labour in dam building as in any other form of water work. Much of your damming will be merely to raise the level of the water, perhaps only a foot if you want to box in a flat creek, perhaps "five or six feet if you want to raise the water on to the creek-bank. In this case there is plenty of water. You do not wish to conserve it, you merely can direct it into your box or on to the ground you intend to work.

Your job is simple. In a heavily running stream, a few boulders rolled here and there between a line of boulders already across the creek will very soon begin to raise the water level. Probably in half an hour you will have raised the water sufficiently high at the point from which you want to lay your fluming to run the water required into your box.

In a stream with less water, throw smaller stones between your line of boulders, with armfuls of bushes and grass. You'll soon raise the water.

Now, about the case where every drop of water is precious, where only a trickle is passing down your creek. Well, for a start, if you only want to raise the level of that water—nothing more—there is no need for a "spout" in your dam. So a main source of worry and loss is avoided. But presume you must build a dam to conserve the water.

No matter what type of dam you are building, look to your foundation. You would not build your house upon sand; but many and many a man has attempted to build his dam wall upon that shifting material. Walk up the creek and look for your old friend the rock bar. You know that is solid bottom. Doubly welcome in this case, as parts of it jutting up to or above water level are going to save you a lot of wall building. If you cannot find a bar, then you must choose a spot where you can see, or feel with pick and shovel, the solid rock bottom. If you were to build a splendid water-tight bank right across the creek, and its foundations were sand and wash-drift, then, as your dam filled, the weight of water would simply squeeze its way through the porous foundation below your wall, and your dam would never rise above a certain level. I have known men on surprisingly numerous occasions spend months on a fine big dam, to find when completed that they had built upon a rotten foundation.

So, even if your dam is only an affair of a few days' work, see that its foundation is solid rock bottom. Choose a site if possible where the banks are high, and narrow in. Your wall will be the shorter, stronger, and will hold more water if you can build the ends into high creek-banks.

Further, try and pick a site where the catchment area is long and flat. This means that every inch you raise your wall, will also raise a sheet of water an inch high that spreads far back along the creek. With such a catchment, a five foot high dam will hold far more water than the laboriously built and dangerous fifteen footer, whose catchment area is a series of falls. An ideal site for a dam is a "bottleneck." Build your wall across the neck.

Having chosen your foundation site, trench straight across the creek, laying the bottom of the trench bare. Clean out all cracks, for these must be plugged water-tight. Shovel or wheelbarrow your loam from the handiest bank, mixing it with grass as a binder and stamping it down as you shovel it in. This is the most important part of the dam wall, this first foundation which takes the greatest pressure.

Now, put in your spout at the centre, and right on bottom. The spout can be a hollow log, with say a three-inch orifice and from four to eight feet long. Make it longer, of course, than the base of your foundation. Where you are about to lay your pipe, ram a thoroughly water-tight bed of loam and grass. Plug your spout down on this, then go on filling up your wall, particularly ramming well around that spout and immediately underneath it, or the water will try to trickle through there when the dam begins to fill. Remember, you do not want to lose a drop of water, no matter on how small a scale you are working. Say that your dam takes all night and half a day to fill, and then only gives you a box-head of water for two hours, you can see that with the slightest leak there will be no water at all.

For the rest, fall a tree from bank to bank. Cut logs, branches, saplings, and lay all longways from the fallen tree down into your foundation. Lay them at a gentle slope, making, really, a close fence across the creek. In between these logs, etc., place armfuls of small branches, leaves, and tufts of grass. A favourite practice is to make two such "fences," and fill in between with stamped down loam and grass. Thus you make the dam wall. If you are going to use the dam for months, it is advisable to make an "overflow," as precaution against flood water. A simple method is to lower by a foot a five foot strip along the dam wall, protecting it with saplings and bark. Over this your overflow makes its get-away. The plug with which you plug your spout requires a little thought, otherwise it will cause you endless bother: it will be a leaky tap on a giant scale. A good idea is to chisel a few inches sloping, down, on the inside rim of the spout. For the plug, use a long stick, with old clothes and bagging wadded around the plug end of the stick, the bagging ends flowing loose. Thrust this stick down the spout from the inside of the dam. The stick protrudes away out down the spout. Tug the stick end. The wadded clothing, that is the plug, thus closes the spout while the growing pressure of the water drives the loose ends of the bagging around the mouth of the spout. To open your dam, just push the stick, and regulate the exact flow of water you require, placing a stone against the end of the stick.

You know now a great deal about boxes and boxing. I will describe my own favourite box and then you will understand as much about box sluicing as I do. This type of box I have used on many fields, on all sorts of ground, and it has saved all sorts of gold right down to fines and caused me no anxiety. When working "pin head" and finer gold I have simply doubled the length of the box; in the second box using fibre matting as a saving device instead of basket work.

This box a man can carry anywhere. He can place it practically in any working position, under awkward conditions, in a very short time. The box is of the lightest wood to be secured in the locality, cork-wood for preference if you get a tree with sufficient hardness of grain. The dimensions of the box are: length, six feet: bottom board, eighteen inches wide at the head end, tapering to twelve inches wide at the tail: side boards, six inches wide: head board, five and a half inches wide. This half-inch difference at the head of the box allows the water to flow straight into the box and saves labour in banking up earth to guide the water in. The box being only six inches in height saves an appreciable amount of clamming which would otherwise be necessary. You have only to raise the height of the water five, and a half inches. Instead of the usual splash-board, cut a thin sliver of deal, say, the length of the head of the box, and about six inches wide. Cut off a narrow strip, three inches long, from each end of the board, so that the board will just fit down into the box: the uncut flanges resting on the edges of the box. Just move this board to the head of the box and you have a splashboard that directs a sharp and even stream straight down into the head of the box. Push the board hard up against the head of the box and it automatically shuts off the water. You see, it does away with the sand-bag you have been using to shut off your water. This form of splashboard can be entirely done without if you wish, but it adds to efficiency and it saves time. Compared to messing about with a sand-bag, it is like pressing an electric button.

The ripples for the box are all of basketwork, easy to make, quick and easy to manipulate, lasting, and sure to save all but exceptionally fine gold. There are two ripples, each two feet long. These ripples fit down snugly into the box. You can put them in place in ten seconds, and lift them straight up out of the box in one movement. At the very tail of your box is the ordinary inch high ripple. Your first basketwork ripple fits in the tail of the box: the second ripple fits in ahead of it. This leaves approximately two feet bare at the head of the box for the forking stones.

For each ripple, you first make a framework, two side sticks each two feet long, two end sticks, and a stick to run right up the centre. Make this frame so that it will snugly fit the width of your box. The side and end sticks as a general rule are an inch wide. The centre stick is generally a two foot length of cane or a stick about the thickness of a whip handle. Such is your ripple frame.

Now get lengths of cane. If you are in scrub country you will find any amount of lawyer cane—the old schoolteacher's cane. If you cannot get cane use pliable sticks from the bush about the thickness of a cane. Poke a strip of cane across your framework, shoving it under the centre stick, its ends resting one on each upper side of the frame. Cut it so and you have the length. Cut a number of canes the same length and split them in halves. Then do the basketwork, one strip of cane under the centre stick, the next strip over, and so on, until you have basketed both your ripple frames. Then drop them in your box and you will at once see that you have a hundred ripples. No gold could escape from that maze.

You will want more fall for this type of box. Set it, shovel some wash into the head, touch the splashboard with your finger and in runs the water merrily. Let it run with a strength that rattles the pebbles down over the basketwork and out at the tail of the box. Shovel your dirt in, fork only when necessary, and put your stuff through quick and lively. Most of the gold, if at all on the coarse side, will stay up at the head of the box among the forking stones. After a day's run you may notice that the spaces between the canes are clogged with tiny quartz sand. Run your knife among the canes. Those cracks get filled exactly as Nature, you remember, fills the crevices in the rock bar.

If your dirt is inclined to be clayey, rig up another box and place it at the head of box number one. In the top box have no ripples. Stir the dirt with the shovel as you work. The clay as a rule will be reduced to mud as the top box discharges down into the bottom one.

Where this type of box is used in New Guinea, the diggers generally have three sets of ripples, with niggers throwing out the forking stones by hand. You yourself can work faster by using a fork, and you don't have to feed and pay niggers. This type of box is used to great advantage in parts of north

BASKETWORK RIPPLE SPLASH BOARD.

2 ft. LONG

A.A. BASKETWORK RIPPLES.

B. SPLASH BOARD.

5½ ins. HIGH.

1 ft. 6 ins.

5 inches.

B.

A.

6 ft. LONG.

A.

6 inches.

ORDINARY 1½ in. RIPPLE.

Box Head raised 5 ins. above ground to represent necessary fall.

Queensland; and, I daresay, elsewhere. It is an ideal one man box; and is just as handy for two men.

This box is often made five or six feet long, one foot wide, and six inches high. These, particularly, are the measurements where a sluicing fork is not used.

A sluicing fork as a rule is about fifteen inches wide. So, when using one you must make the head of your box just a little wider. Always use a fork. You can throw away twenty stones in one operation with a fork to five with your hands. Further, you will use the fork twice to once with your hands and the "fingers" of the fork never get sore or tired.

The idea of the tail of the box being narrower is pure efficiency. If you have very little water then that water shoots the tailings faster out of the narrowed tail than it could do were the water unconfined.

VIII

How to make water work

Now for hints that may save much time and labour in hand sluicing. Except hydraulic sluicing, hand sluicing is the quickest form of mining known to the alluvial miner, either for tin or gold, or alluvial wolfram or scheelite for that matter, or for the exceptionally valuable but rare platinum and osmiridium.

The amount of ground you can put through quickly may mean that otherwise unprofitable ground is payable. Hence, if you are in mineral country near any streams, prospect the country thoroughly before you move to a drier district. The miner who understands water power, always considers that water is almost as valuable as mineral.

If your sluicing claim is cumbered by many and large boulders, as so many streams are, a crowbar is a very handy tool. (You can lever aside a gigantic boulder with a crowbar.) Roll the boulder aside a foot or two and sluice away the bottom on which it is resting. First sluice away the ground on the lower side, then lever the boulder on to this worked ground. You will never want that ground again.

Those last instructions may sound childish; but you would be surprised at the number of men who shift boulders on to ground they must work later and thus have to move the boulders back again.

Think, too, when clearing the ground beneath the boulder. It may be so heavy that the united strength of you and your mate, levering at the bar, fail to shift it. Lever from the uphill side and gravitation will help you. The boulder's own weight lends a hand. Just the right leverage on the right side and it overbalances. Otherwise a couple of horses might not shift it. Some men can make a boulder claim pay where other men would not dream of even attempting to work it. A profitable result is generally put down to "luck." It is not luck at all. It simply means that one man will shift ten boulders with the same expenditure of time and labour that another man uses to shift two.

You may have a lot to learn about boulders; so learn it quickly. They mean dead labour. They take up a lot of ground and you must shift them to get at the bottom. So learn to shift them quickly. Many men look at a large boulder, then stroll to the camp for hammer and drills, gelignite and fuse. They will spend an hour boring that boulder. Then they blast it; and after all have to shift the cracked stone. Don't waste time that way, if you can possibly shift it by "working your head." The same applies to submerged logs, to giant roots—to everything connected with a mining claim. Always remember that for shifting any solid heavy object you have a giant to your hand—the ordinary lever.

Some men put up envied records at shifting ground by sheer strength. "'Long Jack' is a great worker," is a frequent remark in any mining camp. But give me the skinny little chap who works the water with his head. He will shift far more ground than the giant who does not understand properly how to work water.

Perhaps you stake a claim along a creek dammed up into a series of long waterholes, or long flat stretches of creek, by rocky bars. You wish you could hand sluice; but your ground has no fall, so you start boxing.

Here, probably, you can make your own fall. Shoot a tail-race through the bar below your claim.

Make that race two or three feet deeper, if possible, than your estimate of the depth of the deepest hole in your bedrock. Thus you "bring up" the fall necessary to enable you to ground sluice.

Shooting a race through a rock bar is simplicity. You have only to see it done. Get an old hand to explain the boring, charging, tamping, and firing of a hole. Any young lad on a mining field who has watched Dad handle the drills and gelignite, can "shoot" through a bar. So can you after having been shown. But don't get in the habit of clenching the dynamite cap on to the fuse with your teeth. That is a fool thing to do. Buy a proper crimping tool. "Shooting" is not often necessary. It is simple work however and you will soon pick it up.

When starting your sluicing claim, as you bring up the tail-race you may run into holes deeper than the level of your race. You cannot see these holes until you work into them} they are full of gravels and wash. In that case you must deepen the race. If possible it must be slightly deeper than the deepest hole in your ground. Otherwise you could not sluice the bottom of those holes down into the race. With sufficient fall, it only means bringing up the tail-race deeper. However, if the creek is long and flat you may not have sufficient fall to "bottom" the holes. If so, bring up the tail-race without losing the fall necessary to carry away the tailings. Then, as you work up the claim and expose hole after hole, sluice all the overburden off them that you can, then pick the rest of the hole and shovel it into the race. There may be a few ounces of gold in the bottom of that hole; and you want it.

Should you strike a deep hole when bringing up the race, sluice on ahead until you get on solid bottom again. Then come back and shovel the gravels in that hole back behind you into the race.

Clean the bottom thoroughly. Then go ahead into the race and sluice the overburden back into that hole. When that is done, plank it over so as to form a solid race. "Haven't got any planks!" Well, take your tomahawk and rob a tree of its bark.

Always keep your weather-eye open for a "false bottom." Such sometimes occurs. It has all the appearance of the bottom you are working on; but a pebble or two, stuck in it like cement, may put it away. Drive your pick into it. If you strike washstones, investigate further. Almost certainly it is a false bottom. If so, there may be more gold underneath it resting on the real bottom than there has been on the bottom you have actually worked up.

False bottoms are very much the exception. Still, they are typical of some classes of country.

There are mining fields in which a false bottom has given many claims a double lease of life; the gold won from the top of the false bottom, and the gold got afterwards deeper below on the real bottom.

Claims have been worked out and abandoned until some "heady" cove came along, noticed a wash-stone here and there where the bottom should be all rock, sank his pick in, and found a brand new claim with all the overburden nicely removed.

When sluicing in mountain country, and particularly in tropical country, you must understand quite a lot of things about water. Water is really a live thing. It has power: furious strength. You can make it toil like a chained giant for you. But, if you don't use your head, it will wash away your three months' work in a night. If you are working a dam, one night's storm will wash it away unless you have built a strong "overflow" in case of sudden flood.

Ground may be found with a lifetime's work in it. It can be worked profitably by a big dam. In northern parts, men sometimes put two months' work into a dam—as you would do if you found a claim under similar physical conditions. If you have two months' sluicings in your main race, and a sudden storm washes away dam and race, you will lose the fruits of months in a few hours. So, when the thunderstorm season is drawing near, be sure that your overflow and excess water race are in good repair.

With a hand-sluicing claim carrying constant running water, remember that a thunderstorm will make your creek a river. If there is no excess water-side race, deep, with plenty of fall to carry the extra water away swiftly, then your races will be washed away and your nicely cleared ground covered with tailings and debris which you will have to remove all for nothing—not to mention the loss of the gold your sluicing had accumulated in the tail-race. Should a sudden flood in the night catch you unawares, grab the hurricane lamp and run to the claim. Don't fall into the race and break your neck as some men have done; but roll all the stones you can into the race and thus save your gold.

Perhaps you may locate a new creek in scrubby country. Prospect the ground well up and down the length of that creek before you peg out your claim. If no one else is near you, prospect thoroughly for the richest area of ground before pegging your claim. By the way, remember that when you peg and register your claim, you must peg and register your head and tail-race too. There is just as much trouble over water rights in country where the value of water is known, as there are Warden's-court cases over claims.

If you have pegged a claim on scrubby country, of course you must clear the scrub and burn it off before you can set to work in earnest. Learn all you can about water wherever you are. The more you know of the vagaries of water, the more you can chain those vagaries to work for you.

IX

River Work: Osmiridium: Platinum

Many of you will meet rivers in your travels. To prospect a river is a puzzle if you don't know how. The job appears a hopelessly big thing. You don't know what to do with that broad sheet of water. You wonder how gold could be in there. How to go about proving whether gold is in there beats you.

Well, don't move on for a while. Do a bit of thinking. That river is a great traveller. It has come from the ranges twenty, forty, sixty miles distant as the crow flies; while its windings have probably carried it over two hundred miles and more of country. Then, its heads come from far back in the ranges, and probably thousands of creeks, gullies, and ravines empty into those heads, each pouring its quota of water into the river.

Try to visualize the thousand square miles of country those many water-courses intersect. And, remember, they all bring detritus from that huge area of country and concentrate it into the river.

You have earth and stone and gravels and minerals from all that country in the one long winding channel. So, by prospecting that river, you to a very large extent prospect the far-flung area of country it drains.

Every ravine which runs into the river carries down detritus from its particular hill; and ravines from a thousand hills run into your river. If any of those ravines are running down a hill which carries minerals, then some mineral will be washed into the watercourse. It is your job to prospect that river, locate traces, keep prospecting until you find payable mineral in the main watercourse or trace it into some by-creek; and if that is not payable, still trace it away up into the hills. As soon as you know a little about the game, you will find the search a fascinating one.

So travel up along the river towards its head. In the foothills, the water will shallow. The first "bottom" you will see will be your old friend the rock bar, but on a large scale this time. Try the gutters and crevices in this if the water is not rushing over too strongly. In many a river bar you can hand sluice the gutters, which is quick prospecting on a large scale.

Whether or no, travel on up the river. You will find the water shallower as it rushes over bars and ledges. Prospect these bars; and wherever you see a chance of working down to the hard river-bottom, try the bottom of any deep gutter that runs right across the river-bed. Soon you will find a beach, high and dry now. Try that beach. Pot hole it; better still run a cutting right across it and dish the bottom if you can't run the river water into it and hand sluice it. Keep your eye open for "swirls" where the course has once swept in far under a bank. Probably, if any gold at all has come into the river, you will get a few fine colours here and there in these bars, terraces, and corners of banks. Go miles farther up, following the windings of the river and prospecting any "points," where the river comes around a turn. Remember that the lightest and finest of the gold will have been washed farthest down. If there is payable gold anywhere in that river or its creeks or gullies it will most probably be miles farther up, invariably towards the heads of river or creek.

So keep prospecting up towards the heads of the river, treating the water-way as if it were a ravine.

That is what the stream-bed really is, on a giant scale: a ravine that carries the mineral secrets of many miles of ranges.

Try the big creeks that come into your river. If you get colours in a creek, follow it up until you decide which shows the best prospects, the creek or the river. If the creek, then follow up that creek to its source. If the river, then come back to the river. Should a creek come in bearing good prospects, follow it right up. As you travel towards its head you will find the prospects getting coarser until they lead you on to alluvial gold, or into a ravine that is shedding the gold into the creek. Should the gold be shedding from some reef on a mountain side, the prospects will lead you to some ravine down which the tell-tale specks are being shed. There may be half a dozen creeks or gullies shedding gold into your river. It is for you to prospect thoroughly and find the richest creek, or the richest deposit wherever it may be.

So, when you come to a river don't see it as a broad sheet of water that blocks your path. Look upon it as covering, possibly, a long line of traces of gold that will lead you to the "find" of your dreams.

On account of its greater volume a river is harder to prospect and work than a creek. But there are compensations. If you strike payable gold in a river, you have a far larger area of gold-bearing ground on which to stake your claim and the satisfaction of knowing that your find will mean a living for a greater number of men. Also, you have abundant water to hand sluice with. Work your river claim just as you would your creek claim. Pay attention to all river beaches, some great claims have been staked on beaches and terraces. Be particularly careful with cracks across any river-bed. These are often three feet wide and may go down six or seven feet. They are splendid catches for gold. If your river flows through gorge country, remember that a portion of the old bed may be up there, a hundred feet or more up on a hillside. I have been on goldfields where the richest gold has been got in the original old bed up on the mountain tops hundreds of feet above the river.

The stones in practically any river-bed will give you a clue to the country miles away. Say you strike a river running through sandstone country. You notice that some of the washstones are of quartz, of ironstone and granite and slate. Well, that tells you a lot. Those stones have been brought down by the river and prove that miles farther up there is a belt of quartz, slate, iron-stone, and granite country. And you know that such country is "gold country" and worth prospecting.

If you travel up your river and come into slate country, try the river bottom and if you find blue slate clay on the bottom, then prospect the river thoroughly. Very rich gold is sometimes found in blue slate clay, particularly if quartz grit be mixed with it. Should the bottom of your stream yield "rusty" iron gravel, be on the lookout for gold in the near locality. Rusty iron wash is always "kindly" wash.

Pipeclay on the bottom is a promising indication too. So are black iron sands. Black iron sands do not mean that you are bound to strike gold there, not by a long way. They are merely a promising indication.

There are other valuable sands as well as gold sands. You may notice in your dish, at some time or other, steel-grey (probably flattish) grains of a heavy mineral, heavier even than gold grains. You have difficulty in washing these steel-grey grains out of the dish, you notice that the gold grains will wash out before the grey stuff. Those steel-grey grains are, almost certainly, platinum or osmiridium, both more valuable than gold.

Platinum grains as a rule are flattish, very heavy, of a greyish silver colour. Osmiridium is more "steely." I have seen osmiridium look for all the world like chippings from a pick. Say you have been picking up a race, the bottom of which is exceedingly hard rock. You wash a dish. There is no gold in it, only a grain of steel that has been broken off the pick point. That dish is not a duffer for it has taught you what osmiridium looks like.

At ordinary times, platinum may be worth £10 per ounce, osmiridium from £12 to £16 per ounce, depending on the quality, quantity available, and demand. But the price of both minerals fluctuates.

Osmiridium is sometimes worth £35 per ounce. Both these rare minerals are used in the manufacture of scientific instruments, electrical instruments, wireless, etc. Osmiridium is also largely used in the tipping of fountain-pen nibs.

I have mentioned platinum and osmiridium, in case you should come across these ordinary looking grains of stuff in your dish and throw them away. That has happened comparatively often: it has happened in Tasmania. That State produces most of Australasia's osmiridium. The very profitable

Adam's River field is the best so far discovered. Osmiridium was, for many years, frequently thrown away in Papua, the diggers cursing the dull grey grains that would not wash away from the gold. On the Gira and Yodda river fields, for instance, the diggers detested the stuff because they had to pick it out with their fingers when they were separating the gold. An old German quietly bought the metal for years. The diggers declared he was mad. Osmiridium provides a chapter in the romantic life of one of New Guinea's best known prospectors. The mineral rose to a sky high price during the war years and this prospector remembered those detested grey grains thrown away on one of the abandoned fields. He vanished into the jungle for twelve months and returned with some thousands of pounds worth of the steel-grey metal.

Who knows but that platinum and osmiridium may have been similarly thrown away on long forgotten Australian fields. Anyway, you are wise to both minerals now. You prospect for and work both minerals as you do gold. They are invariably associated with gold, you don't have to search for them separately. Simply prospect for gold, and if you are panning off in any creek that carries platinum or osmiridium you will find them in the dish. That is if you scrape out the bottom of the cracks and crevices properly.

Platinum, besides being found in inland alluvial deposits, is sometimes present in black iron sands on sea beaches. Osmiridium, in Papua, mostly occurs in serpentine country. Gold occurs largely in serpentine country in Australia. Remember, wherever you find one mineral, there may be found the others.

X

Secrets of Alluvial Gold

Now, many of you are going to work old ground. Much of the gold has gone, but if you can hydraulic or hand sluice, you will be pretty right. Should physical conditions make your ground impossible to sluice, then you must utilize all the knowledge you can get hold of to make it pay.

Here are some secrets of gold which will literally produce gold for you if you are a trier. And, remember, what I am about to tell you applies to "old" ground and new alike. In fact it applies to practically all minerals, and gems too.

In every worked field there has been ground left, mainly because the men working it believed there was no more mineral there. But no man can see one half-inch into or through the ground.

The tailings and headings of some old fields have been worked over and over again. Much mineral has escaped in the tailings due to the inexperience or carelessness of the men working, or the inefficient apparatus used for saving the mineral sought. Gems even are thrown away in the mullock. On the opal fields, particularly those of White Cliffs and Lightning Ridge, thousands of pounds worth of precious stones have been thrown on the dumps. In the boom days of only those two fields quite a number of men did nothing else but sit on the big refuse heaps, scratching down the opal dirt with one hand and picking up their finds with the other.

If you get any solid ground in any gold (or any mineral or gem) claim that has produced rich results, you are practically certain to do fairly well. Some mineral will have been left in the solid ground. I am referring, remember, to a claim which has produced rich mineral, not to a claim on the outskirts of the once rich ground. Worked ground, of course, will be cumbered with piles of stone, pitted with shafts and old workings, most likely covered with undergrowth.

When you have looked round a bit, look at the timber. Are any giant trees standing? Often diggers will work completely round a tree, leaving it standing. Its great butt and roots will cover a lot of ground. Well, I have seen quite a lot of gold and tin recovered from underneath old stumps and trees; and have myself got some jolly good gold that way on abandoned fields. But be careful! It is dangerous work undermining a big tree. Don't get yourself pinned down.

Quite a lot of solid ground covered over with forkings and stone heaps has been left in old claims. You must use your head and muscles in finding these, and other, blocks of solid ground.

If you have been "laid on" to old ground that once was rich, have a go at the bottom. You know a great deal about the bottom of a mineral claim now. What you have read in an hour or two in this book was not learned in a year. It took me a good many years to find out what I am telling you. If the men who first worked your claim were new-chums, there will certainly be gold left in that bottom for you. Providing, of course, you have not been forestalled by thoroughly experienced hands.

In underground workings solid ground is in blocks and pillars: blocks of ground left because the old hands thought there was not sufficient mineral in them to pay for taking the blocks out, or because in those rich days the mineral did not appear rich enough for them, and pillars (of ground) often left as supports for the roof.

However, underground work in abandoned ground is often dangerous. I strongly advise you not to go underground in old workings unless you have an experienced underground man with you. Underground workings in bad country are possible death traps to the inexperienced.

We will return to the surface. You will be safer there, and it is at surface work that you will start your practical experience.

Now I will explain how men miss gold under the most favourable conditions—even thoroughly experienced men who earn their living at gold-digging. And remember that all written here applies to new ground as well as worked-out ground. If all the worked ground I write of had only been worked as I am trying to teach you to work it, then comparatively little gold would have been left behind. Realize that if you are working a new mineral claim and you do not pay the strictest attention to the bottom, then you, too, will leave mineral behind for others to recover later. Unless you have the luck to work on a new rich field, you will want all the mineral you can possibly recover to make your ground pay.

I will visualize five fields in particular, all surface sluicing fields worked under the open sky under most favourable conditions. Two of these fields have been worked for thirty years, three have been worked for twenty and are still being worked. The creeks and gullies are practically bare, all timber and overburden long since removed. In some of the creeks you can see the bare bottom for a mile. There is nothing hidden. And yet year after year these same creeks produce gold, gold once thrown away by carelessness, through inexperience, or through the sort of experience that is confident it can learn no more; and also gold left in solid ground away up on the banks or in side ravines where no gold "ought" to be.

Most of these creeks are wet season ground, the diggers dry-stack in the dry and wash the ground through during the seasonal storms. I have found gold in the barest of these long dry creeks, and got appreciable quantities of gold from them after they had just been cleaned up after the wet. Now, in those long stretches of bare bottom there was not supposed to be a penny-weight of gold left. In reality there were ounces of gold in every gully, all in a few dishes of dirt.

Remember, no bottom is even. In each of those bare creeks the bottom had a thousand little depressions, scooped out holes, broken down bars, broken down crevices, scooped out cracks, levelled off "bumps," picked up "swirl holes," broken down ledges, and the thousand and one other inequalities of bottom. In the last phases of cleaning up, every creek I have in mind now had been swept bare with brush brooms. Yet there was gold left in every one of them.

Here and there, in tiny patches from a foot to an inch square, perhaps only a quarter-inch thick, were little smears of "cement" glued to the bottom. This "cement" was exactly the colour of the bottom otherwise the man who had cleaned that bottom would never have left it there. Ever wary eyes had to find those little splashes of cement. Often it was only their sandy texture that betrayed them, or a wondering scratch of the pick. Sometimes, rather often, all I got was sufficient "dirt" to fill a couple of matchboxes. But there was gold in that dirt. I have shifted a ton of dirt, at times, and not got a grain of gold in it.

You see, a million of years ago when that cement was forming it was sticky mud, it held on to gold grains and encased them and then fastened itself on the bottom.

On the "lips" of ledges which had been broken down and cleaned there were quite often little slithers of cement to be found; and here and there were rusty little blobs of caked iron sand. All was carefully scraped off and went into the dish or sugar-bag. It would be a good day that would fill a sugar-bag. But by Jove there were a few ounces of gold in it!

A fruitful deposit of gold for me in a number of sluiced out creeks were tiny "boil holes." Often, it was only two or three grains of gravel that betrayed them. At times just one solitary speck of quartz gravel, one tiny speck of iron-stone pebble, would betray a hole. I'd gouge it out with an iron spike and scoop out the dirt with a spoon. You see, those boil holes are formed where one spot in a hard bottom is soft, the water "boils" out the soft, leaving often a circular hole perhaps an inch in circumference and six inches deep. Then the ever working water fills that hole up again with gravels. It keeps working, boiling the lighter gravels out and filling the hole again with heavier and heavier gravels and gold grains. These finally get jammed like a cement core and the water covers them with clay or cement. The digger comes along, cleans up the bottom, but his shovel scrapes over the boil holes and leaves them there. It is only the experienced and careful searcher who finds them.

Always be especially careful with boil holes under a ledge or bar. There are a hundred bars in any creek, perhaps only six inches or a foot high. Treat any layer of outstanding rock that runs across a creek as a bar.

You understand that water falling over a bar has a decided drop. It will certainly scoop out a hole, perhaps a wide and deep one. Even if the rock is very hard it will, almost certainly, find some soft spot or fault and boil out a hole. I have found, under a ledge, boil holes a foot wide and three feet deep. Under a big bar there may be a number of these holes. Under a big creek or river ledge a boil hole may be five feet wide and seven or eight feet deep. These holes (great catches for specimens) are filled with tightly wedged wash stones, quartz and ironstone pebbles, black sands, and gold. I have got pieces up to five ounces weight in some of these large boil holes, and that too in creeks that have been worked by experienced miners for years.

Be on the lookout also for "swirl holes." Towards the sides and banks of a creek, the water in sudden floods being turned aside by rock or bank, swirls round seeking a getaway and gouges out the soft bottom, filling it in the course of time with heavy gravels and gold grains, and covering it finally with clays. These swirls often gouge sideways under a layer of rock: the water finds a soft spot under that layer and leaves it on "the surface." So, though your pick touches even flint-hard bottom always be sure there is no wash-filled swirl hole underneath.

Examine all bars even though broken down with the pick. Experienced men are by no means always alive to the depth to which grains of gold will wedge down a crack, or under layers of apparently firm but one time really broken rock (broken by upheaval or other forces of Nature). At times, if observant, you will find, in a creek-bed, the apparently solid bottom to be, in patches, really layers of rock. Lift up these layers with the pick and sweep up even the dust under them. In numerous sluiced creeks, here and there up the creek, are a few loads of gravels, left as being not worth cleaning up, or deposited there by a late flood after the creek was cleaned up. Well, shovel away a yard of the gravels on the top or head end of the patch (towards the head of the creek) and try the bottom. In that way I have often quickly got an ounce or two of gold.

On parts of the bottom, particularly if it is rough and hard, you will find little holes here and there perhaps only a marble's depth. An occasional rock ledge may be honeycombed with these "pit" holes, quite invisible except to the man who is looking for them—the man who walks very slowly up a creek, with his eyes all around him; who drops on his knees and crawls about peering into every ledge, scraping here and there, seeking every gravel-filled cavity. These pit-holes, too, are wedged with tiny pebbles, often covered with cement or clay, often with dust disguising the clay. Scrape out every such hole and put all in the sugar-bag.

The sands you are now collecting are really concentrates, the gold showing from coarse to fine. You will be surprised at the coarse pieces that can wedge deep into the tiny holes and cracks. Carry your sugar-bag of dirt to the nearest waterhole and dish it. If the water is a few miles away and you have an old packhorse, save your dirt until you have a packhorse load and then pack it down. There will be mighty little dirt, so you can easily dish it.

As for the rest, learn something new in every creek you try. You will never cease learning of the cunning hiding-places that grains of gold will find. Although I have told you much, there is a lot I do not know. Every man finds out "new" things for himself.

For working an old creek in which water is running, the same rules apply. Pay attention to the bottom as I have explained in hand sluicing, and you will get any gold that is left. I have seen nuggets of gold, even, recovered from under boulders that old hands have left as being too much trouble to shift; and in "false" bottom and in patches of wash that have been left for some reason or other. Often in the banks of a worked- out claim rich gold and tin have been recovered.

This chapter should teach you how important it is to thoroughly clean up every inch of bottom when you are working solid ground in a new claim.

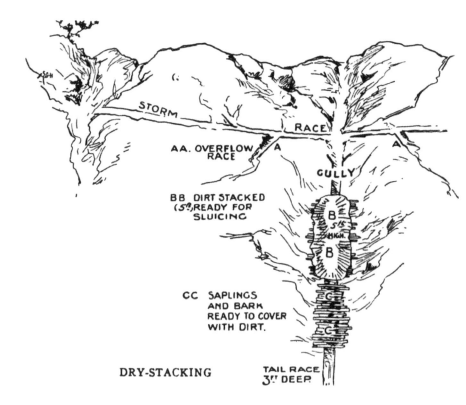

STORM RACE

AA. OVERFLOW RACE   A   A

GULLY

BB DIRT STACKED
(5°)READY FOR
SLUICING

B

B

CC SAPLINGS
AND BARK
READY TO COVER
WITH DIRT.

DRY-STACKING

TAIL RACE
3" DEEP.

XI

Dry-Stacking

Now, you may be prospecting in dry country. Only enough water to boil your billy within miles. You find a dry creek that carries payable prospects. If you "only had water!" Well, it rains, doesn't it? Even in the driest areas there are seasonal thunderstorms, if no regular wet season. Almost everywhere in Australasia every dry gully "runs" at least a few times during the year. Right. You will "dry-stack." Pitch your camp by the nearest cooking water, and set to work— providing you have the wherewithal to buy tucker for a few months. If not, then mark the locality well in your memory and return say three months before the next wet season. That ground may be good. It may be highly payable even for a cradle, if you only had water. How much more payable then could you command running water to rush it through! There are numbers of such localities in Australia. Men have prospected there and gone away, longingly, shaking their head: "If I only had water to work that ground!" Dry-stacking means loosening ground with the pick, preparing it, throwing away the stones, cutting a race, and when a storm comes and the gully "runs," rushing the dirt through. It is the simplest form of hand sluicing. You understand it thoroughly, for by now you have mastered more difficult forms.

I will give a few hints to show you that, here again, you will win much more gold in any given time if you think before you start in to work ground, and if you think before you abandon ground.

There will be running water for only a few hours at a time, during storms, should your gully be in a particularly arid region. In an ordinarily dry region, after the first storms have soaked the ground, your gully will run for a few days, a few weeks, a few months—it all depends on how dry the country is. With such a gully, see the good thing you would have walked away from!

Let us take first the arid, practically "desert," gully which only runs when the storm is actually raining. Your prospects have shown you that the gold is on the bottom. Right, you can throw all overburden aside. Start in the gully just below where the gold ceases to show payable prospects, and bring up an ordinary race, right up the centre of the gully to its very head. Don't touch the bottom wash. Throw the remainder clear away. Come back, and take up the bottom, simply throwing it on the bank beside you. Dry clean the bottom thoroughly of course. Then go back and bring up the race. Make it three feet deep and two wide if the digging is easy enough. Don't forget to bring up your fall as you go: you will want plenty of fall so that the dirt can be rushed through when the water comes. Of course, throw away the rock from your new-dug race. Then throw into the race the "bottom" that you deposited on the side of the race, throwing some of the wash-stones back as well, to save the gold.

Now go back and strip right up the gully, stripping, of course, only ground that you know is payable. Strip right down on to the bottom wash. Throw the strippings away across the bank so that the rains won't wash it back into the race. Again go right back and "loosen up" your wash, the bottom this time, throwing all the stones away, so that later on you will not have to waste golden time forking them. Up along both edges of the race, throw the wash into the race until it is nearly half full, but no more. The object in taking this strip of wash up both sides of the race, is that you want the bottom there bare, on which to rest the ends of the light logs and strips of bark crossing the race. Lay your saplings across the race along its entire length. Then, as you pick out the bottom (still throwing away all stones) shovel your picked bottom on to the saplings.

At the end of a few months, you will have a long high heap of bottom wash running the entire length of the gully. Under the wash is the bridge of saplings; under the saplings the race.

Now, think awhile. You can increase your prospective water-supply enormously. Make Nature help you, she will only help if you harness her. The head of your gully runs up towards the crown of a hill, perhaps hills. There are a score of gullies all around that hill, hundreds of them if you are on a chain of hills. Well, rob a dozen gullies of their water to come. Run a "storm-race" right around the crown of the hill, and make both ends of this race, running on a slightly downward slope, of course, run into the head of your gully. Thus you collect all the water that falls on that hill. After the ground is "soaked" by the first shower or two, your long storm-race begins to run and you have a sluice-head of brown working water pouring down your gully where, without that race, it might still be bone dry. If the first thunderstorm produces a decent downpour, you will have a rush of water right away.

Near the head of your gully, on both sides, dig "cut away" races leading from your storm-race. Thus you have control of the water. A sand-bag (filled and ready) thrown into the storm-race sends the overflow raging harmlessly down the hill. Otherwise, your desert gully will be turned into a sea and your wash-dirt and gold washed away.

Immediately the first storm comes, grab your hurricane lamp and run out. If the water is gurgling and splashing down the race let it get a "go on" until it has levelled the dirt already in the race. Then start from the head of the race and hurry down, pulling out a log or sheet of bark every six feet or so. The dirt pours down through the opening to be immediately swept along the race. Pull out a log here and there to the very end of the race; then run back and repeat. Pulling out the logs in this fashion ensures a steady and even stream of dirt falling down into the race.

By that time the storm is over, but if you have cut a long storm-race you may well get another two, three, or four hours out of it. You can put through a tremendous quantity of dirt in an hour by this method. If you get flummoxed at all, or anything goes wrong, grab the long handled shovel and pour the dirt heaps into the race. Go your hardest. Don't worry about stones or saving gold or anything: just scoop that earth into the race while the water lasts. Fill in time waiting for the next storm by scraping your disturbed dirt back on to the logs again, so that you will have a flying start when it comes.

As to cleaning up, there will be almost certainly a waterhole handy for a week or a month after the wet. If possible, make provision beforehand for a handy "hole" down below in your gully, throw a dam just below some hollow or depression so that it will hold water.

The dirt left in your race you simply carry to the waterhole and cradle it: "wet jig" it, or dish it as you prefer. If running water is away below you,

you box the dirt of course. That is how you can work by water-power in dry country. Don't bother to pave your race, unless the gold is fine. If you pave portion of the race, it inevitably holds back a lot of earth, which is all left for you to clean up very likely by the tedious dish.

Now, perhaps, you are prospecting in average rainfall country. No water handy for a mile or two: perhaps the nearest creek is five miles away. You locate a fair-sized area of ground, creek, or gully. It does not matter what the ground is so long as you locate payable gold in it. You have done a bit of sluicing and you feel aggrieved when your mate sighs and says: "If we only had water we could work this ground. We haven't a hope of making it pay, though, with water five miles away."

Now, before packing up and moving on, use your head. Mahomet might have had to go to the mountain, but you can make water come to you. Are there any mountains handy? Good-oh! The proposition is almost a certainty. If there are no mountains, are there any hills? Yes. Here too there is a chance of bringing the water on. If the big hills are too far away, don't look blue, make for the nearest running creek. If it is five miles away, never mind, so long as you are sure of those prospects.

Now, if the level of the nearest creek is not already higher than your ground, can you raise that level (by a dam), so that the water would be a few feet higher than your distant ground? If so, and your ground has the necessary small fall (it almost certainly will have) then your immediate problem is solved. All you have to do is to cut a race from the creek to your ground and so bring the water on.

You must take levels first. That is simple. A triangle with a plumb-bob will do it. But you may well be in country where men are quite unused to sluicing, and you, perhaps, are one of those greenhorns with no confidence in themselves. You feel you are not capable of bringing the water all that distance "on your own." State your case to the nearest mining inspector, or write to the Mines Department. They will very soon look at your proposition and give you all necessary advice.

Say there is water in a running creek half a mile away. Your eye alone tells you that up the creek a bit is a fall well above the level of your ground. You and your mate can easily bring the water on by "making it follow" you. Start your race, allow water to run in, then shovel from it. So long as the water follows the shovel, you know you are on a level that will bring it right to where you want it. Water won't flow up-hill. Numbers of men have tried to make it do so, either through carelessness or a mistake in their levels. In country where sluicing is universal, there is bound to be some abandoned race, perhaps three miles along, that had been cut "up-hill."

Even if levels have been taken, it is always advisable after you have cut a few chains to give the water a run. If it runs easily along the race, you know all is well.

XII

Wet Season Claims

—Prospecting For Old River Beds

Yet another type of country is that in which even the main creeks only run for three or four months in the year, but during that time they run constantly. If you locate payable ground near such a creek (with water for only part of the year), and if your ground has the necessary fall, then you will have a "wet season" claim. Don't be afraid of a claim that you can only work for a few months of the year. Many a tin and gold claim is a wet season claim.

It depends, of course, on what you have learned. If you have prospected your ground thoroughly, estimate how much, if you had the water on, you could put through in a month. The question then will be: "Is it worth the labour of bringing on this water, when the claim will return me such an amount in a given time?" Answer the question yourself.

In your wanderings you possibly locate a large area of ground, showing poor prospects. Although the ground "averages" well, it is a bit too poor for you to trouble about. Besides, the nearest supply of running water is seven, eight, why, ten miles away. Foolishness to waste time on this ground!

But, wait. You may have "company's ground." It is useless to you, but you may sell it. The man of capital can afford to bring water on to that ground; and he will if prospects are right.

Now, in prospecting, remember a golden rule about gold: "Where it is, there it is!" It may be anywhere. That is the reason of "New Chum's Luck." The beginner, expecting to pick up gold specks like big yellow plums, will look for the metal in places that the old digger might laugh at.

Gold is not only in watercourses and depressions. It is usually there; but it may be up on top of a hill: a "patch" of it may run down a hill-slope: it may be deep down under solid rock: it may be "on the surface;" in the "grass roots;"

in the "tree roots." Don't laugh. Many hundreds of ounces of gold (and some big slugs) have been found among tree roots. If you are in gold country and see a tree uprooted by a storm, try a dish of the quartz and rubble clinging to its roots. Then try a dish as deep down as you can shovel from the hole. That old tree may have been resting upon a much older river-bed.

Gold is in grass roots, too. I have seen a tuft of grass shaken into a dish and the little gold "pieces" roll away from the loam. That is when, of course, the grass is growing upon a "surface patch."

Try any ironstone ridges you come across, especially if quartz is littered about. If you get "fly specks" in your dish, then try all over the place, higgle-dy-piggledy. Pay particular attention to the slightest "gutter" where the last shower of rain has washed down. If you get on a "lead" of colours, follow them right up if necessary to the very crown of the ridge. They may well lead you to the cap of a reef. If not, then trench the crown; criss-cross it and dish the bottom; sink a few potholes along the crown; there may be an old water course buried "under" below, even though you got your traces of gold on top. The same rule applies to any hill-side on which you get colours.

In gorge country, or country subject to landslides, cast your eyes up now and again. You may see a seam of wash far up in the side of a hill. Perhaps you only distinguish what appears to be a clump of wash-stones. Impossible for wash to be there when the river is flowing a hundred feet below! Not at all. Climb right up and try that wash. There is where the river flowed a million years ago!

Try the ground around any big old ironstone outcrop, especially if there is quartz about. If you see a patch of rubble anywhere at all, try it. It is some-times an "indication" of gold. Try all ravines. Wherever you see decomposed slate with a sprinkling of quartz or ironstone, try that slate. Try ledges in creek or ravine, even if it be up in a hill, so long as you are in likely country.

You may see a layer of wash-stones exposed right on the crown of a moun-tain. I have seen numbers; old river-beds of ages past left high and dry in the course of time. You very soon learn to recognize wash-stones by their smooth, often rounded, shape. It does not matter what colour they are. Dig in the centre of them until you come to hard rock bottom. Try your luck often! A river-bed on the summit of a mountain seems ridiculous. Never mind.

Remember that the river-beds you particularly wish to find are those which were running rivers millions of years ago. Those are the real "alluvial beds."

Perhaps you come across a body of conglomerate; that is, a mass of wash-stones cemented together, generally quartz cemented by iron. As a rule, conglomerate is very hard. Try to sink through it and prospect bottom. Occasionally, conglomerate carries a little gold all through.

Often, gold is patchy. If you are on a patch and it "cuts out," don't throw up straight away. Prospect your ground "checker-board" fashion first. It may contain half a dozen patches.

Perhaps you are working a broad creek. You are getting a little gold. You are disappointed. You feel that more ought to be there. Well, always try the banks. Sometimes there is richer gold under the banks than there is in the creek itself. The old original creek may once have flowed where the banks now are. Mountains have fallen, have buried the old creek, and the creek you are now trying is really a "new" creek. Remember, this world is very old, and gold was born when the world was young. Therefore search for it in the old, old places.

Are there terraces in your creek? Many creeks have no terraces. These are flats really, running back from a creek, along either side. Much rich gold has been got from terraces. The creek, in that long ago when it was really a river, twisted and turned where those terraces now are.

To prospect a terrace, put a line of pot-holes across it. The surest way is to trench right across it. You will almost certainly cut an old bed and quite possibly a lead. As you know, a lead is a gutter of wash carrying gold—or alluvial tin in exactly the same way.

Big flats (perhaps quite away from a water-course) are at times really the overburden topping an old river-bed. There may be nothing to indicate that a watercourse flowed underneath. Only shaft sinking will prove it. Possibly you notice a long hollow in the ground that may be a guide. And you notice a wash-stone, a river-stone, sticking up under a tuft of grass. Well, if you pick up a water-worn stone away from a watercourse, it is worthwhile scratching about for another one. Then sink down and see if a river-bed lies underneath.

A shaft over ten feet deep will need a windlass. You can make the whole thing with the aid of a tomahawk. Then you only need the rope and hook and oil-drum bucket. Make a bucket out of a bag, if you are only sinking a pot-hole or two.

If, however, you get encouraging prospects and determine to set in properly, here is the most up-to-date windlass, and so simple that a school-boy could make it.

The cylindrical barrel of suitable diameter you saw from the trunk of a tree. Into this barrel put an iron handle (preferably one at each end). Bore the end of the barrel, and hammer in the handle. Then drive a heavy nail or "key" through the barrel and through a slot in the end of the handle. Thus, if you are pulling up your mate the windlass handle cannot slip out and let him down with a run. The barrel, at the handles, rests in "dog-legs" (crossed sticks) or a wooden frame set above the shaft. Each end of the winding rope can have a bucket: the empty bucket goes down while the full one is being hauled up.

From the shaft bottom, you have to "drive out" the wash. Haul it. Use one side of the windlass as a dump, the other side as a "wash paddock." When your paddock heap is big enough, cart it to water and box it.

Tunnelling is worked on a similar system, except that you need no shaft. You tunnel when you strike wash running into the side of a hill. Tunnelling is faster work than shaft-sinking and driving. Naturally, both methods are a hundred times slower than open work sluicing. In "driving" a shaft, or in tunnelling, you only save the bottom wash. You clean up the bottom, too, exactly as in surface work. If you sink a shaft and bottom a duffer, but on wash, drive both ends of it and cross the old bed in an endeavour to pick up a gutter.

"Screening" is often used in the slower methods of mining. This simply means throwing the wash against a large standing sieve, to free it of stones. If you are in dry country and putting your dirt through a distant cradle, or box, you can screen to advantage; because you do not then have to cart the unnecessary wash-stones. You can only screen dry ground. Make your own screen—a frame of saplings, with No 8 fencing wire in criss-crossed strands as the screen.

Mining laws. There are laws for alluvial and reef claims, sluicing claims, hydraulic claims, leases, etc.: laws for water rights and tailings rights. They vary slightly in different States. So before you set out, be sure to buy your Miner's Right (without which you have no legal right to ground) and a copy of the Mining Laws. The Miner's Right usually costs 5s. per year, the Mining Laws, Is. 6d. a copy. The "Laws" contains much useful information, including measurements for differing ground. For instance, you can take up much more ground for an hydraulic sluicing area than you can for an ordinary alluvial claim. And, remember, should you locate payable new ground, even if only a mile or two away from the nearest worked ground, then you are a prospector and can apply for a "Prospector's Reward Claim." If you locate new country ten miles away from the nearest field, you are entitled to a still larger claim.

Now as to the vexed question of "new-chum's" gold. This will hardly trouble you. There are numerous varieties of new-chum gold; mundic, copper pyrites, arsenical pyrites, iron pyrites, yellow cubes, golden mica, etc.

You know lead, don't you? Well, if you are in doubt, compare your gold to lead. Take your sample and try to push a pin into it. If you did that to a pellet of lead, the pin would penetrate a little, and you would see the shiny lead. Do the same to gold, and you will see the shiny yellow.

You can scratch lead with your pocket-knife. So you can gold and see the glint of yellow. Put a pellet of lead on the flat of the axe, and hit the pellet with a hammer. It will flatten out. A pellet of gold will do the same.

But if you scratch any "dud" gold, it won't scratch at all, or else will give any old scratch. If you bang it with the hammer it will fly to pieces and most likely flip you in the eye.

As to golden mica, the "gold" you see shining up at you whenever you cross a creek almost, well, you know that gold isn't in sand. It is on the bottom. Also, you can scratch that mica to powder with your thumbnail. If you wash it in the dish, it will float away.

You are not likely to mistake alluvial gold. Once you see it in the dish you will always know it. You are much more likely to be deceived by copper pyrites in a stone. But by the time you begin to look for reefs you will know the difference between copper and gold.

Any stone which appears to you to contain mineral (after you have been prospecting a while and know a little) show to an old hand or send a sample to the Mines Department. But your main object is alluvial gold, in which you are not troubled by stones, except forkings, and possibly specimens. If you are troubled by specimens, welcome the trouble.

XIII

Hydraulic Sluicing

Now for the quickest, the most effective, the most interesting, the most highly payable form of alluvial mining in the world—"Hydraulic Sluicing by Gravitation."

Hydraulic sluicing will wash away mountains.

You may laugh when you realize that men have actually cradled dirt that they could have worked by hand-sluicing. It is a fact, too, that they have cradled dirt they could have "blown" away by hydraulic power. You would do just the same if you did not know. Remember that the dish and cradle are the slowest methods of mining for gold. So, as always, think before you set in. Work your ground by the quickest method that the physical conditions of the ground will allow. Learn hydraulic sluicing and apply the method when you locate suitable ground.

Don't picture by the word "hydraulic" huge masses of clanking machinery. Hydraulic mining is simplicity itself. You can rig up a plant as well as I. Don't picture "Capital" and "Big Men" with "Money." I have set up a first-class hydraulic plant at a cost of £100. I know a hundred men who have put on a plant at a cost of £50. I know plenty who have put on a handy workable plant at a cost of £20.

A plant that costs £1000 is a whopper. That plant may have only the working capacity of your £100 one, the extra cost is in wages, race cutting, or greater length of pipe-line necessitated by differing contours of the ground. An hydraulic plant operated by gravitation, working a Giant nozzle, is estimated to do the work of at least thirty men: far more, in certain types of country— in gravelly sluicing ground not too encumbered with boulders, for instance. This means that ground you would abandon as not bringing you in tobacco and matches, may be highly payable under a nozzle. You see, that nozzle puts through at least thirty times the amount of ground per day that you do, so the amount of gold won from that same ground is thirty times more!

Hence, if you are on ground that is bringing you in £1 a week, and you can put a nozzle on—£30 a week may go into your pockets.

Now, I'll explain "hydraulic" sufficiently for you to understand clearly. Then I will explain a little plant, costing from £20 to £30, which you can manipulate and lay anywhere you like on your claim. This plant will do the work of from ten to fifteen men. It won't have a Giant nozzle: you can have that if you give £25 for it. By all means get the Giant if you have the water pressure necessary to work it. It will be the cheapest £25 you ever invested. The nozzle we shall use meanwhile will be a bottle, any old bottle will do if we haven't a few bob to buy a brass or copper nozzle. Failing anything better, we'll make a nozzle out of a piece of tin.

Three conditions are necessary for hydraulic sluicing by gravitation.

First, your ground must have a little gold in it. Ground that "averages" gives the best results for hydraulic, especially a big face with a "colour" or two here and there right through it. The quantity of ground put through is what pays.

Next, you must have "water pressure." That means, to put the matter simply, you must be able to bring your water on a higher level than the ground you work. Say your ground is near the foot of a hill. Can you bring your water race along the hill up above the claim? Can you bring it twenty, fifty, one hundred, two hundred feet vertical?

Twenty feet will just work our canvas hose providing the ground be soft loam and sand: forty feet will give our hose a jolly nice pressure: eighty feet will make the Giant rumble throatily: two hundred will make him roar.

Engineers generally say so many "lb. pressure." But on an hydraulic sluicing field the term generally is so many "feet" pressure. There is a little difference between the lb. and foot pressure. We will stick to the foot. It is easier to understand. A Giant also is often referred to as a Monitor, while the nozzle-man who works it always calls it "the Gun."

The third requirement for an hydraulic claim is "fall." You know all about fall. It is the same exactly as in hand sluicing.

Do you get the idea? You must bring water on for hand sluicing. Whether you bring it along a three mile race or three yards from the creek, you must bring it on. But water has only to flow over your ground to enable you to hand sluice. For hydraulic, you must have your water at a considerably higher level than your ground.

Your "intake," that is, where you set the water into your pipe-line, can be half a mile away, but that intake must be higher than your ground. Within reason, the higher the better. Height, from the intake to the nozzle tip, gives the water its working pressure.

A sluice-head (say) of water pouring into a large intake rushes down a pipe-line and its own weight forcing it out of a very narrow nozzle gives the jet cutting power.

The pipe-line, also, is simplicity itself. For the most powerful pressure generally used (200 feet) the gauge of iron is eighteen, that is, eighteen gauge galvanized sheet iron. On northern Queensland fields the "hose" man uses the same iron and size of pipes. They can put a Giant on to their pipe-line any time they wish, should they get the pressure.

Numbers of men, however, especially if they have a small claim soon to be worked out, don't bother with a Giant nozzle. The Giant is the only heavy part of a plant. These men, with from thirty to sixty feet of pressure use twenty-two gauge iron; it is lighter, not so stiff in the making of the pipe, and the finished pipes are very light to carry about. A consideration when a man's claim may be half-way up a mountain. When he shifts his pipe-line he can lift a couple of those pipes on his shoulder and climb over the rocks like a mountain goat. The eighteen gauge iron is light enough though. I can carry two pipes up a mountain any day, and I am only a weed. Also, when once you have made your pipes of eighteen gauge iron, should you later shift your plant to a different locality which gives you a greater water pressure, you can immediately put on a Giant nozzle.

The pipes are generally made in three feet lengths of seven and eight-inch diameter. Three lengths joined together make a pipe. The intake pipe is larger, up to twenty-two inches in diameter, to admit a good volume of water at the start. The intake pipe tapers till it fits nicely to the first eight-inch pipe. Then you have a line of eight-inch pipes, as many as wanted. Each pipe is made just a fraction smaller at one end than the other. This is to enable one pipe to be gently forced into the other. At the end of your eight-inch pipes is a "reducing" pipe. This reduces down from eight inches to a shade under seven inches.

Thus its snout fits into the butt of the first seven-inch pipe. These in turn fit into one another.

It is quick and easy work laying a pipe-line from your intake down on to your claim. Like everything else done, you do the job properly. The ground down the hill-slope is uneven. There are contours to be dodged, gullies to be crossed. Try to lay the line as straight as possible, firmly and evenly on the ground. When you come to a gully, build a rough trestle across it—a "bridge" for the pipe-line to rest on. Across hollows in the ground, your pipes must be supported on logs or a trestle. Remember, that pipe-line will soon be full of water under pressure. If your pipes are loosely fitted or unevenly laid your whole line will leap and buck and fly into the air like a string of maddened sausages. When they "blow out" you must rush up-hill, turn off the water, wipe the sweat from your brow, have a good swear, and lay your pipe-line all over again; more carefully this time.

When laid, especially if you are going to use say 100 feet of pressure or more, place a light log across the lower end of the pipe-line, say across any portion of the line where it looks a bit "weak" due to some inequality of the ground. Be careful if you are compelled to use an "elbow" in your line. An elbow is a short length of pipe; well, like an elbow. It is used where the pipe-line must turn off at an angle. A hillock may compel you to use an elbow. Remember, when the pressure is on, the force will strike that elbow. Drive stakes down beside it so that the pressure won't blow it out of connexion with the line.

Each pipe fits into the "mouth" of the one in front, say one inch. Some men solder a rivet an inch back from the rim of each pipe. This is to prevent "telescoping," that is, water pressure driving a pipe clean down into the other. But the rivet is unnecessary, unless a very big pressure is used, say from 150 to 200 feet. Even then the precaution is not always used. Sometimes handy lugs are riveted on to each end of each pipe. When the pipes are joined, these lugs touch, a bolt is inserted through a hole in each, and a nut screwed on with the fingers. The pipes are thus easily tightened against any pressure or trouble. Such precautions are hardly necessary unless working with great pressure.

Another precaution is an air-valve here and there on a pipe down the line. Here is the simplest valve in the world. Cut out of the pipe a piece an inch long and half an inch wide: bore a hole through one end: hold a piece of leather against it and pierce a similar hole through the leather, with another hole in the pipe close to where you cut the iron, but on the intake side of the hole: shove a tiny bolt through leather and piece of iron: place both inside the pipe under the hole: push the bolt up through the hole: screw on the nut and there is your air-valve. As the pipe fills with water the valve is pushed up close, as you would push up a trap-door with your hand. When your "run" is finished and you turn off the water the valve drops and lets air into the pipes.

The idea is to prevent air suction flattening the pipes like pancakes. That happens very rarely. If you turn your water off at the intake on the instant, then the water still in the pipe-line as it rushes down to the nozzle is liable to suck in sufficient air to flatten a pipe or two, or to do the opposite and cause a vacuum. But you need not bother about such queer tricks of Nature. If you turn your water off slowly, pipe-flattening can't happen. Even these simple precautions will not be needed under say 130 feet of pressure. One hundred feet of pressure will cut very hard ground.

XIV

Hydraulic Sluicing

(Continued)

Now, as to the making of these pipes. The firms from whom the iron is bought at the ordinary market price per ton, cut the iron in three-foot lengths and roll it. These lengths are a handy size for pack-horses. On North Queensland fields, for instance, the iron has to be packed thirty, forty, and more miles to the different fields. Hence, made pipes, of lengths of nine or twelve-foot iron, could not be packed. But if you located a claim not far from a railway-line and accessible by dray, any ironmongery firm would put the pipes together and you would be saved the trouble, but at added cost. Further, made pipes are bulky: you would have to pay for their space. Whereas the rolled, unsoldered sheets all fit into one another and do not take up a tenth of the space.

The rolling of the iron is about the only job in pipe-making that you would find hard to do. Otherwise, you could buy the iron on the nearest cowshed, straighten out the corrugations and make your own plant right there from A to Z.

Eighteen-gauge new sheet iron, being stiff, is put through rollers. The end of the sheet is placed between rollers very similar to those on a mangle: a handle is turned and the iron is thus "rolled."

It comes out rounded, so that by hand alone you can press the ends together into the cylindrical shape of a pipe. Otherwise, imagine the difficulty you would have with a stiff flat sheet of iron!

So, get your iron rolled in three-foot lengths, all ready to solder and rivet. Now here is a tip if you are an inexperienced man with the snips. All sheet iron, no matter what size, is a certain length and width. But your pipes, no matter what size, must be a shade smaller at one end than the other. If you riveted your pipes as the iron came, the ends of all the pipes would be the same. They would not fit in.

Explain to the firm from whom you buy the iron that you want it cut to size. You want sufficient iron to make so many hundred feet of eight-inch pipe, so many hundred feet of seven-inch pipe. Also that you want one intake pipe of eleven- inch diameter to reduce down to a shade under eight inches. (If you prefer it, you can have any number of pipes reducing from your intake: the number is immaterial. Some men have a notion that if the reducing of the pipes from the intake into the eight inch is done by longer degrees, the pressure is heavier. However, please yourself.) You want another reducer, a pipe to reduce from eight inches to a shade under seven inches. This reducer connects the eight inch pipes to the seven inch. Then you want the most important reducing pipe, the "Reducer," from your seven inch into your nozzle. Now, if you use a Giant nozzle, you have no reducer, the seven inch fits into a reducing attachment on the nozzle. But I take it you are going to make your own nozzle, or use a hose. So you want a reducing pipe to connect from the seven-inch pipe and reduce down into the hose. The diameter of your reducer is seven inches, tapering so as to fit two inches or more into your hose. Now, if your hose is to be three inches diameter, your pipe must taper to, say, $2^{3/4}$ inches. This should allow two, or better still three, inches of the reducer to fit into the hose. You need to get more of the end of your reducer into the hose than you do of the main pipes into one another. The hose must have a very strong grip. It receives all the pressure; and unless it can be fastened very strongly over the end of the reducing pipe, it will "blow away."

Before ordering your reducing pipe, note the diameter of your hose. Common sense tells you that if your hose is of two-inch diameter, then the tip of your reducing pipe must be If inches. Don't make the usual mistake and order one the same diameter as the other. If you do, it means a little extra trouble. You must make an attachment to fit the hose on to the pipe, or sew exceptionally strong canvas into a very short length of hose to be sewn on to the main hose and then over the reducing tip of the pipe. If this attachment continually blows out, serve you right for not using your head.

To make your own hose, simply sew a double length of strong canvas together in the shape of a hose. The diameter is immaterial: so is the possible fact that you are a mug with a needle. But home-made hoses only last two or three weeks. The pressure, the constant dragging over gravels that cut with the action of the water, wear them out; and when they burst you either get the stream in your eye or under your tail. More about hoses later.

So, when you order your pipes, send the firm the measurements, and ask that the iron be raddled "8 inch," "7 inch," "Intake," "Reducing."

Thus you will have no snipping to do, and as you pick up the short rolled iron sheets you know exactly what pipe you are going to make, by the raddle mark. Tar is best. But, remember, your iron will be all in three-foot sheets, and that in every three sheets one is slightly smaller. Don't rivet this sheet into the middle of a pipe; otherwise you will find that it does not fit into the end of its mate. If your firm is obliging, and you ask them, they will raddle or tar mark each set of three sheets "8 inch 1," "8 inch 2," "8 inch 3." And so you put these three sheets together: the "1" is the big end of the pipe, the "2" is the middle, the "3" is the small end. The three sheets joined together make the one complete nine-foot pipe. You see, simplicity itself.

If you wish to trim your own sheets, as many men do, there is nothing to prevent you. It only means snipping a long, very gradually broadening slither from each three sheets, so that when the iron is riveted into a pipe one end is slightly smaller than the other.

One cannot give the exact measurement for a complete line of pipes. You may need 900 feet of pipes; whereas the man farther down the creek or up the hill may only need 300; and the man a mile or two away needs, possibly, half a mile of pipe-line. It all depends on the contour of the ground, and the distance from your intake to the nozzle tip.

You need not stick to any one measurement for pipes, some men use eleven inch, ten inch reducing to nine inch, then eight inch, then seven inch. Lots of claims use a twenty-two inch or even larger intake. If you use a Giant nozzle, the last one, two, or three hundred feet (as you wish) must be seven inch so as to fit the "gun," as the nozzle is generally called. In the main, the longest length of a pipe-line is contained in seven-inch pipes. Thus if your pipe-line is to be 500 feet long, you will need 300 feet of seven-inch pipes, 200 feet of eight-inch, an intake pipe, a reducing pipe to connect the eight inch pipes with the seven inch, and your main Reducer to connect the seven inch to the hose.

Men with a hose are quite independent of the size of pipes. Their biggest pipes may be seven inch reducing to five inches, and of a lighter gauge of iron than eighteen. But I believe in seven inch as your smallest pipes, because then you can always fit them to a Giant if opportunity occurs.

You see, you can please yourself to a large extent. But if you are going to use a hundred foot or over of pressure, make your smaller pipes seven inch, of eighteen gauge iron.

When ordering pipes, make provision for a hundred feet more pipes than you require. Then, as you work out the "face," you turn off the water, take off the reducing pipe, put on three lengths more of pipes, shove in your reducer, and are working again in ten minutes twenty-seven feet nearer the "face." Spare pipes save you half a day or a day's work shifting the entire pipe-line.

Order also, two or three "elbows," of various angles. An elbow is hard to make, because it consists of very short strips of iron cut and soldered together to form an elbow or angle.

You use an elbow when you cannot run your pipe-line in a direct line, or when you wish to sluice ground at a different angle to the direction in which your pipes are laid. Generally elbows can be done without; but they are often useful, and on occasions necessary.

Now your hose. This is the most important part of your plant. The hose must be strong. I advise you to buy a sixty-foot length of fireman's hose, with bronze or copper nozzle and tips attached. Have the hose cut in half with couplings attached. The advantage of this is that after sluicing a face for a week, you can, without shifting your pipe-line, hitch on the coupling and in another minute have the hose going with another week's work ahead before you need bother about spare pipes. Another great advantage of a hose is that you can move it anywhere. You command a sixty-foot radius of ground around you. You can work an extraordinarily large "face" that way— poke into all corners and crannies of the face.

A lesser favourite than a Giant or a hose is a hydrant. Most probably you have seen the Fire Brigade using one. For hydraulic sluicing, a long brass nozzle is screwed into the Fire Brigade hydrant; but the coupling to the pipe is on a different scale. The hydrant costs £5 10s. and will laugh at 100 feet pressure. Unfortunately, it cannot be directed at the face with the same ease as a hose or Giant, and, unless in a sluicing district, the correct type of hydrant is difficult to obtain. However, you know what a hydrant is now.

SLUICING HILL OF DECOMPOSED GRANITE WITH HYDRANT

A Giant nozzle is like a gun acting on a swivel. You can turn it around and direct the jet of water at any angle, but you can't pick up that Giant and carry it sixty feet away. Of course, a Giant will laugh at 200 feet of pressure. But you need a strong hose indeed to stand more than fifty or sixty feet constantly.

The fireman's hose is fitted with an ideal little nozzle, on which can be screwed half-inch, one-inch, $1^{3/4}$-inch, and two-inch tips as you wish. The one-inch tip is universally used. It gives pressure, cutting power, and water. The larger tips throw a much "lazier" stream and are used to advantage on a "tall" face of loam or soft overburden that you want to rush away.

The best hose of all, though of course a dear one, is a length of that heavy, wire-bound rubber hose you see the municipal people using. This wire-bound hose stands a far greater pressure than any canvas hose, and has a far greater life. It can be dragged regardless, almost, over a rough bottom.

If you buy a strong canvas hose, you can lengthen its life considerably by sewing hessian around it. When the hessian is worn out sew on more hessian and your hose will have a long life.

Now, say you are starting with only sufficient pounds to buy a few hundred feet of light pipes. If you have no money at all, and you can get hold of any light sheet iron, cut down a sapling, bark it, and trim it carefully to the full length and shape of a pipe. Bend your iron to shape over this, hammering it into shape with a wooden mallet. That is your first pipe. You need not even buy rivets. Double over both edge lengths of the iron (hammer them to shape down the edge of a square iron rod) and clench these "lips" together. Make your own canvas hose too. For a nozzle, you can cut off the end and neck of a bottle and sew that into the hose. Better still, a two-foot length of light iron. Shape it around a cylindrical piece of wood. Make one end just round enough to fit snugly into your hose. Bind the hose around it tightly. The other end, out of which the stream of water will gush, is smaller, say roughly to an inch diameter. This is the "tip" of your nozzle. So you are "set."

XV

Hydraulic Sluicing

(continued)

A simple idea that will save you endless trouble is to bolt two lugs on the end of your reducing pipe. To the end of your hose fit immovably a metal ring, or a three-inch length of pipe, a home-made coupling in fact, with two lugs attached. Just slip this over the mouth of the reducing pipe, put a bolt through the lugs, screw each nut on, and your hose is firm with no more trouble. If it is too much trouble to fit this simple device, then wire your hose tightly to the reducing pipe, hitching the wire also to the lugs.

Now as to riveting the pipes when you get the iron. Again, simplicity itself. The hydraulic sluicers do the entire job under a bough-shed: their tools a snips, soldering iron, punch, hammer, and iron bar.

To a stump, or waist-high post sunk in the ground, fasten say a five-foot length of railway-line, trolly-line, round iron bar, length of iron pipe, or whatever is handy. This is a "rest" to do the riveting on. From a rafter, have hanging an endless length of chain. Make it endless by wiring the ends together. A long loop of rope will do. As you join your pipe together it grows to nine feet in length and this is awkward to handle without that loop. Put through it, the pipe is kept level, is out of your road, and swings any way you like.

To make the first three-foot length, put your sheet of iron over the iron bar. The sheet being rolled, is already an unjointed pipe. Overlap the sides say half an inch and with punch and hammer punch your holes, say, an inch apart. The holes finished, place a rivet on the bar, put your iron over it, tap the iron and the rivet comes through; tap the rivet and you have it clenched; and there is your first rivet done. Repeat the operation with two other lengths and you have three three-foot pipes. Now rivet these together into one nine-

3 FT

MAKING HYDRAULIC PIPES

foot pipe. This time, of course, you rivet the ends together. Remember how your sheets are numbered, so that the smaller end of the sheet is made into the smaller end of the pipe.

After riveting two lengths put one end of the finished piece into the loop, fit in the third length, and swing the part to be riveted over the bar. A child's fingers can manipulate it.

Now for soldering the joined pipe. You simply solder the seams. They are already drawn right by the riveting. Some men rivet very closely and do not bother to solder. But if you are going to use heavy pressure, solder as well. Then there is no chance of losing water. Simple enough, isn't it?

Lay your pipe-line, of course, from the intake of your "head-race" (a head-race is that race which brings you your water-supply) straight down to the "face" where you are going to "blow in." Now, get a light stick and fork; tie one end of a cord around the nozzle of the hose and the other end to the stick. Keep the stick upright, resting the free end on the ground. The nozzle then hangs six inches or a foot from the ground. Adjust the string as you require. This arrangement saves you the trouble and awkwardness of holding that nozzle in your hands all day. With stick and string, you can direct the water jet on to any portion of the face you desire. You can smoke at the same time, or scratch your head. And there is not the slightest fatigue from handling the nozzle.

Use the fork to hold the stick when you wish to leave the nozzle. The stream will play on to the face and wash away ground while you shift a log, or roll away a boulder, or do a bit of forking.

When you set a new pipe-line, don't turn the water into the intake with a rush. Take a few minutes to turn it on. Otherwise, if there is a fault in your pipe-line through faulty laying, it will blow apart. With a slow stream of water running for a start, as the pipes begin to fill, water will quickly jet out from a faulty join, and you have ample time to straighten the line or put a log over the particular pipe to "steady" it.

Leaks do not matter much, so long as you have plenty of water. But if water is scarce, you must stop them. Simple. Rub handfuls of dry grass between your hands, and throw the fluffy stuff into the intake. This is sucked down the line and suction draws it into every join, soon making the entire pipe-line completely water-tight.

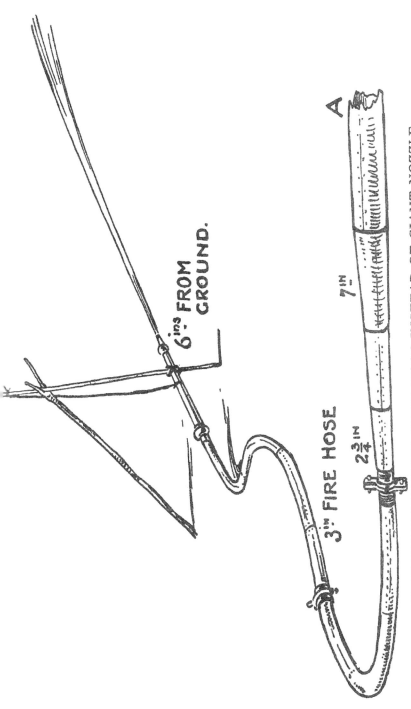

A

7th

6^{ins} FROM GROUND.

3^{in} FIRE HOSE

2$\frac{3}{4}$^{IN}

HYDRAULIC SLUICING WITH HOSE INSTEAD OF GIANT NOZZLE

Now for the working power of pressure. You can work even with twenty feet of pressure. But this will only wash away soft loam or friable sandy banks. Of course, it will work up a creek-bed or sluice away any shingly beach on a river-flat. Thirty feet of pressure does good work with a made hose. I have seen many a creek claim worked out with under thirty feet of pressure. Forty feet will cut ordinarily hard picking ground. You are "set" if you have an ordinary claim and forty feet of pressure: it is a lively hose pressure that will cut away wash very quickly.

Now, wash varies. There is hard wash and damned hard wash. Then there is cement wash. It takes 150 feet of pressure to pound away hard set cement wash or conglomerate. You don't meet it very often. If you do, bore under it if possible: that is, direct the nozzle jet under it. Possibly it is just a layer or bed of hard wash. Undermine it, and down it comes with a crash.

Sometimes resting on bottom is three or four feet of wash too hard for the pressure at your command. Don't say: "I wish I could get pressure on to this creek: that wash would pay. It wouldn't pay for hand sluicing. I'd have to sluice away that ten feet of overburden on top of it."

Well, get as much pressure as you can, and hydraulic sluice the overburden away. Then hand sluice the wash. Very likely it will pay that way. If the overburden is light stuff, the hydraulic will rush it away. Then, direct your nozzle stream (to save you cutting races) wherever you intend to hand sluice the hard bottom wash.

With a hundred to two hundred feet of pressure you can sluice away a mountain, providing it is not solid rock. Do not imagine, as so many do, that big pressure is "Company Pressure." Not in the least. You can work as big a plant as a company any day, providing you have the ground, the pressure, the fall, and the little capital necessary to install the plant. Then you put on wages men and work three shifts, with carbide light at night. The claim pays the wages sheet. That is the ambition of all sluicers in the north. Plenty of men have attained their ambition.

Now, as I have already said, hydraulic is the great power that makes poor ground pay. The greater your area of ground, the deeper its depth, the less have its gold or tin contents to be for the ground to pay. A number of factors enter into consideration. For a very big poor show, you must have heavy pressure, plenty of water, and a deep face—the deeper the better if a little mineral is scattered throughout. If the face is full of huge boulders that necessitate handling, then those boulders automatically lessen the value of your ground. You have to spend time handling them. Timber is not of so much account, not in a big claim having a deep face. If the surface is covered with scrub, fall it and burn it off. Make a good job of it. All unburned logs as you work up will crash down with the earth into your paddock, and you will have to shift them. So convert every log you can into ashes before you start sluicing. The stumps of course come down and they must be shifted too. Apply the knowledge you gained in boxing and hand sluicing. Think before you handle boulders and timber, and you will only have to handle each once; perhaps not at all. Very often you can sluice; can direct your stream of water under a log or boulder and "blow" the wash away from underneath, without having to handle the obstruction at all. That cannot often be done in hand sluicing.

Mineral is funny; whether gold, tin, or any other valuable metal. You may find a hill-side with a poor prospect of gold running through it. Perhaps the "gold strip" runs right into and through the hill. It may be a thousand feet long and a hundred feet deep. The gold, though very poor, prospects from "the grass roots down." That is an ideal hydraulic sluicing claim. There may not be a bed of wash in it. No matter, so long as the gold or tin is there. Always prospect decomposed granites or slates or diorites. Some famous hills have been decomposed granites with light prospects of mineral right throughout a huge strip: Lode Hill (alluvial tin) for instance, in northern Queensland. Abandoned long years as "worked out" by box men and surface hand sluicers, it brought a fortune to Elliott and Starving who, later on, learning of hydraulic sluicing, brought the water on three miles and put a plant on that "worked-out ground." They worked three shifts for some years before selling out to a company. There are plenty of "Lode Hills." So, always study alluvial ground from every aspect before you give it up as unworkable.

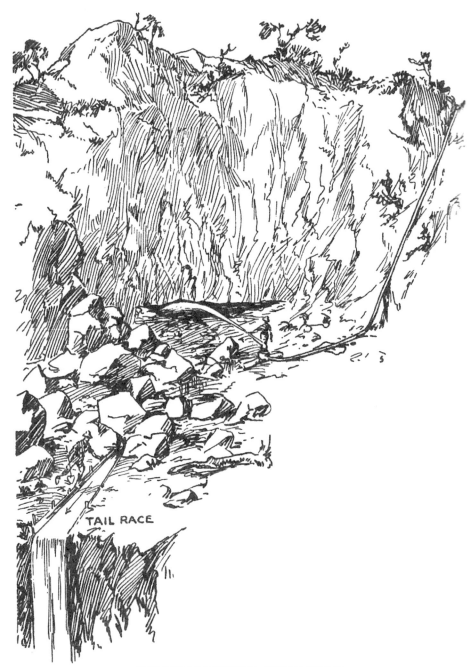

TAIL RACE

UNDERMINING HILLSIDE

XVI

Hydraulic Sluicing

(continued)

In hydraulic working, the object is to undermine the face and bring down "a fall." This fall is a fall of earth. The higher the face, the greater the fall. Down she comes in many tons. "Set" your nozzle to keep boring low down in the face while you clear the paddock of logs and boulders. By that time the fall has all washed away and you start undermining again. If you are working "mates," then your mate will be constantly employed forking stones. Your main race, of course, is wider than in hand sluicing, in order to carry the extra water. If you worked comfortably with a two-foot wide race at hand sluicing, you would want a three-foot race with a hose, if working gold. With a Giant on, you would need a much wider race: five feet for tin, wider still for gold. It depends on the pressure as to how much water your jet is forcing through. Your race must be built to carry the water and at the same time give either tin or gold a chance to "settle." Keep the race flowing evenly. Send away that quantity of ground which keeps your water well mud-coloured, but at the same time is neither mud nor slime. Both these would carry away any fine gold they might contain.

Most of your gold will collect in the paddock. This, i n a n h ydraulic claim, is always before the face. You work the face as wide as the limits of the gold-bearing ground and the radius of your nozzle, allow. The water and sluicings are rushing down from the paddock into your main race. The paddock will be sprinkled with stones, boulders, and wash-stones; and these form a great "catch" for either gold or tin.

Perhaps your overburden carries no gold. It is the strip of wash below that pays. Well, remember your hand sluicing. Strip off the over-burden and rush it through under the nozzle. Strip a paddock as far and wide as the nozzle jet will reach. Then turn the water pressure off a little and "blow into" the bottom. Next, put on a few spare pipes, and blow into the overburden again. Cleaning up is the same as in hand sluicing, only you have a series of far bigger paddocks to clean up. Numbers of men work their paddocks as they go. They blow in for a week; then when necessity compels the lengthening of the pipe-line, they clean up the paddock, turn the water off quite a lot, and blow the paddock sands and concentrates down into the race. As they fork out the stones in the paddock the gold gathers into the rivulets formed by the sluicing water, and into the natural depressions, grooves, channels, and cracks in the bottom. When the paddock is nearly bare they clean it up carefully, scraping out every crack as you did in hand sluicing. Then they dig their race straight up through the cleaned-out paddock into the centre of the face, fix their extra pipes, and blow in again. They do not clean up the main race for a month or two. Sometimes they put lengths of boxes in the race, "rippling" them. It is easier then to clean up. After carefully reducing the race, they wash the concentrates down into the boxes.

Now you know quite a lot about the power of water. Remember, Australia is almost a new field so far as hydraulic by gravitation is concerned. You are going out into a new country in one manner of speaking: for old mineral districts, providing they can be worked by hydraulic, are really new. One cannot believe that only in isolated cases in Australia, can country be found suitable for hydraulic. There are mountains in every State; running water in comparative abundance. Now that you have a practical working knowledge of hydraulic, apply it if you come into "worked out" country. Let the old hands scoff at the "new-fangled" notion. There is nothing new-fangled about it. New Zealand has been the home of hydraulic for many years. Tasmania has worked great poor mines with it. Numerous fields have been given by it a second lease of life. Take the Cooktown tin-fields for instance, Rossville, Mt Romeo, Shipton's Flat, Home Rule, China Camp, Mt Finlayson, Mt Amos, and a number of other fields in the same district: abandoned fields all given a second and highly prosperous life since "hydraulicing" "came in."

INTAKE

UNDERMINING RIVER BANK WITH GIANT NOZZLE

Hydraulic is proving highly successful on the lately discovered Edie Creek and Bulolo fields in the Mandated Territory of New Guinea. It is a success wherever tried. On the Russell River goldfield in northern Queensland for years it sluiced away huge overburdens of solid basalt, just to get at the old river-bed underneath.

Don't forget hand sluicing if you cannot apply hydraulic. Few of the Papuan fields were actually rich, some of them would never have paid had not the men utilized the water; even then a great amount of the work was done by boxing. The diggers in Papua and New Guinea use niggers as labourers. But a white man can shift as much ground as five kanakas any day. Many whites will shift as much ground as ten natives.

Don't get confused with hydraulics by machinery. Your line is hydraulic by gravitation. True, that is machinery; but machinery which you can make and apply yourself. Don't trouble about the other: it is too expensive at present. When you find payable but level ground that would require machinery to raise water to a height, or a large area of level ground with no fall, don't walk away from it. Remember, the big man will buy that ground from you quick and lively, providing, of course, his mining engineers prove it as "payable ground." He will probably put a dredge on it.

I will just mention another phase of hydraulic by gravitation that may help you. This will lift your wash from a low level up to a higher. Say you locate a large alluvial flat containing payable gold or tin. You have more than sufficient water to sluice it. By gravitation you can bring that water along a hill to the needed height for pressure. But the ground you wish to work is perfectly flat, and the bottom you want is ten or fifteen feet below the surface. The job seems utterly hopeless. Your knowledge of hydraulics shows no way out, the ground is "company's ground."

Here is another apparently insuperable disadvantage (we will put the two together in this ground just to show that a little knowledge of hydraulics may mean great things for you). You have sunk pot-holes criss-crossing that flat, in your prospecting work. All those holes now have two or more feet of water in them. Indeed, you cannot bottom some of them, the water has come in so fast. The ground is impossible to work: not only is there no fall for tailings, underneath is a swamp!

Well, in hydraulics by gravitation, providing you have sufficient head pressure, and providing you have more than enough water to work a nozzle, you can work an Elevator. It is this very simple arrangement, which if granted sufficient water and pressure, can be made lift your ground up to surface level. That is, of course, to varying heights, as you will understand by studying the chapter on elevators. The height of the lift being governed by laws of height, pressure, water, and plant.

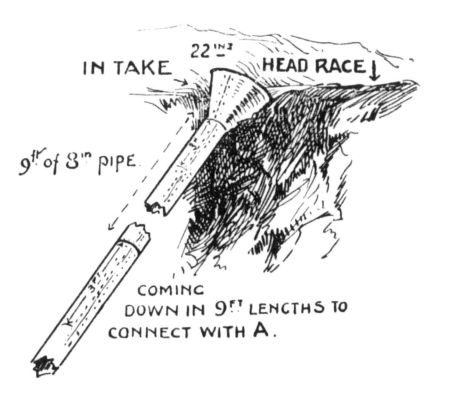

XVII

Elevators

An elevator can be very simply made in your bough-shed. It only means another pipe-line, with a "neck" and a valve in the mouth of the elevating pipe, a "throat." This elevator will suck up not only the excess water in your claim, but all your tailings and wash; and deposit the stream high up in a line of boxes on the flat. There are several simple kinds of elevator; one is worked by suction with a water jet; another uses a jet to blow the tailings straight up the pipe.

To start such a claim, you must first hand-dig out a large paddock, strip it right down to the bottom. There will be your first face into which the nozzle blows. As you dig the water collects in a "sump" hole. Your elevator is sucking or blowing up this water as you work the paddock down. When the paddock is bare to the bottom, sink a hole in it with a race from the face leading into the hole. Start your nozzle working as usual. The tailings rush into the hole and are blown up the elevator into the box race away above.

All is very simple. You can make everything yourself. I am indebted for the drawing and description of the simple elevator described below to Thompson's Engineering and Pipe Co. Ltd., Castlemaine, Victoria. In the drawing, however, I have added a "throat," so that you may understand the term when used.

"To operate an elevator satisfactorily the supply-head should be not less than four or five times greater than the lift from the bottom of the sump to the bottom of the sluice-box. Every two gallons of water from the main will then lift about one gallon from the sump. If the supply-head be eight to ten times the height of lift, so much the better, for then each gallon from the main will lift a gallon from the sump. The delivery column discharges into the bottom of the sluice-box which is placed at a sufficient height above ground to allow the tailings to flow clear away.

"Usually for an outfit of this kind a seven-inch supply-pipe is made to fit a three-inch nozzle tip. The delivery column has a diameter of eight inches and is fitted with a liner at the bottom end to take the wear due to the rush of the tailings. It is very important to centre the jet with the uptake pipe, and to adjust the distance from the distance is usually nine to twelve inches. With such an elevator some twelve cubic yards of tailings per hour may be lifted into the sluice-box."

That is a simple elevator you can make with but little trouble. If you are shifting more than twelve cubic yards per hour, you may need the suction-jet type of elevator we used on the northern tin-fields. This is the same as the one described above except for the throat. Experience compelled us, however, to send for the lower iron pipe which formed the throat. Our elevator would lift all the tailings a two-inch tip, working under a pressure of 150 lb., could flood into the sump hole.

There is another elevator designed by J. Ewing, the hydraulic engineer whose improved methods are widely recognized as being largely responsible for the second lease of life gained by the great Otago goldfields, New Zealand. The fields had been "worked out." Wash still went down, but could not be raised. Well, elevators raised it.

There must be similar ground that "can't be worked" in Australia. You must always think in improved methods: always seek means of shifting more ground in less time. The added gold or tin you win will quickly pay for the necessary plant. Don't growl that a man can't do anything without money. Numbers of my mates started with only the pick and dish, and ended up by owning plants and employing men. They did it by using their brains.

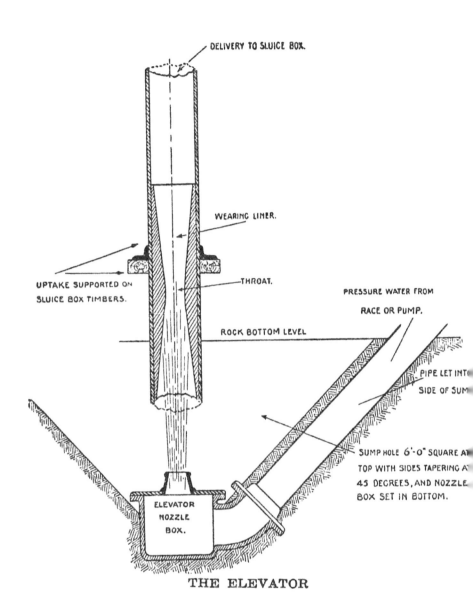

DELIVERY TO SLUICE BOX.

WEARING LINER.

UPTAKE SUPPORTED ON
SLUICE BOX TIMBERS.

THROAT.

PRESSURE WATER FROM
RACE OR PUMP.

ROCK BOTTOM LEVEL

PIPE LET INT
SIDE OF SUM

SUMP HOLE 6'-0" SQUARE A
TOP WITH SIDES TAPERING A
45 DEGREES, AND NOZZLE
BOX SET IN BOTTOM.

ELEVATOR
NOZZLE
BOX.

THE ELEVATOR

The elevator consists of an upright iron tube, its lower end resting some feet below the "bottom" of the ground to be operated upon and in a pit excavated for the purpose of receiving it. The tube is of a diameter proportioned to the height it is intended to elevate the wash dirt, and the quantity of water to be employed. It may be seven, fourteen, twenty-four, or more inches. The upper end of the tube is on a level with the sluice-box into which the raised material is to be discharged.

The tube is of wrought-iron or steel, except at the upper and lower ends, where hard iron castings are used—at the top, for deflecting the debris-carrying stream into the sluice; and at the bottom, to take the wear of the ascending alluvium, which is greatest where it first impinges on entering the tube and for a little distance up.

The tube is supported on stanchions, and narrows from about eight feet above its lower end to about two feet from said lower end, where the contraction ends in a throat, about nine inches in length and of a section from one-fifth to one-third of that of the tube itself, from which the tube again expands to form a bell-mouth on the lower end.

A jet of water is fixed to play straight up the tube through the throat; this jet being connected by pipes of suitable diameter.

To do the best work there must be certain ratios between the diameter of the elevating jet, the diameter of the throat, and the diameter of the uptake pipe; and these again vary with the pressure. Such adjustments having been made, the jet elevator will lift to a height of twelve per cent of the pressure on the elevating-jet (in addition to its own water—that is, the water of the elevating-jet) a similar quantity of water used in breaking down and bringing debris forward to the lower end of the tube.

There is sufficient space left by the bell-mouth between the throat and jet for the water and sluiced material to get in and be caught and whirled up by the ascending jet. By a proper arrangement of parts, water and sluiced material may be lifted to a height equal to thirty or even forty per cent of the pressure on the elevating-jet. But the proportion of water that can be raised will vary in inverse proportion to the height elevated. The variation in the amount of solid material that can be elevated is inconsiderable.

So there is your elevator. In New Zealand, using two elevators the wash dirt has been lifted over a hundred feet.

The elevator pipe is supported by crosspieces and trellis-work. The boxes, built up on trellis-work, reach out over the bank above to receive the elevator discharge.

There is very little indeed now that you do not know about old-time, and the most modern, methods of winning alluvial gold. You understand alluvial tin, and wolfram, too, for that matter. Methods of prospecting for and mining alluvial tin are precisely the same as for alluvial gold. Tin, though, is easier to find and work than gold. But it is not worked by cradle: numbers of men banjo it. However, get your mind off those methods, don't use them unless absolutely necessary. Remember, many of you are going into country that has been well cradled. The cream of the gold has long since gone. But much of that ground is still rich if only you can utilize your knowledge and apply sluicing methods to it.

As regards alluvial tin. It occurs exactly as does alluvial gold. Its usual colour is blackish-brown, and looks very like "black sand" in a creek. You will be deceived by far more forms of "new chum tin" than you will by new chum gold: there are so many varieties of black sands. Once in tin country, however, you will very soon learn to distinguish tin when you see it. Remember too, it is not always black. There is brown tin, amber tin, ruby tin, wood tin, etc. But you will very quickly learn to distinguish tin as readily almost as you will gold. Remember that any heavy black mineral which will grind to a white powder is probably tin oxide. As a general rule, tin oxide will grind to a white or a pale brown powder.

Many thousands of tons of tin have been won by sluice-box; far more by hand sluicing; far more still by hydraulic. In boxing, only one ripple is used, and that in the bottom end of the box. The same with hand sluicing. There may be only one ripple—a barrier of stones eighteen inches or two feet high right at the end of the race. If your race has such a big fall that you have to cut it into a series of races, you will only want one ripple at the end of each race. Use no extra saving devices as you would for gold.

In cleaning up a box, reduce it by forking the stones and throwing the sands repeatedly to the head of the box. The tin is sinking while the sands flow away. Take out a ripple and reduce again until the sands are at a level with your ripple. Take out the next ripple, and so on. With tin, you may be working three, four, or more, inch ripples one above the other at the bottom of your box; making really one ripple of varying height as needed. As you see the tin concentrates showing up black at the head of the box, so you put in another inch high ripple at the tail of the box.

When you are down to the last ripple, only tin concentrates are in the head of the box. Now you have to work a bit. Grab the streaming shovel. This is an ordinary long-handled shovel, with the point cut off straight and half an inch of the sides turned up. With this, scrape right up the bottom of the box, taking every grain of sand in the shovel's width.

Keep throwing the concentrates to the head of the box. The last of the sands, the heavy black iron sands, keep running away out of the tail of the box. (With a little practice you will be able to "stream" tin so that not one ounce of black sands remains in a hundredweight of tin.) Turn off the water, shovel the streamed tin into a handy dish or boxes, then spread it on the tent-fly or bags in the sun until dry. Bag and sell. A sluicing race is cleaned up on the same principle.

From now on have full confidence that you know a great deal about alluvial tin and gold.

XVIII

Dry-Blowing and Nuggets

From the rush and roar and tearing away of hills by the hydraulic sluicer, we will come to the other extreme—the little cloud of dust above the dry-blower. A dry-blower is used where there is no water, not even a muddy hole. It is an ingenious machine, efficient in its environment.

Some men swear by dry-blowing. And as you wish to be a fully experienced alluvial digger, the process and the machines are explained in this chapter. But, remember what I have said about water. Only in very few areas of Australia will a year pass without thunderstorms. So if you visit a dry-blowing field, reasonably sure of a few storms per year, see if you cannot use your water knowledge. By the way, I have seen men using dry-blowers when there was actually running water within a few miles.

Dry-blowing, besides being tedious, loses fine gold, unless you are an exceptionally expert worker, and have a very efficient machine. I feel sure that in Australia there are abandoned fields, dry-blown, in which there is abundance of good ground waiting to be worked by storm-water.

You know the method. Cut your races; then cut your water races over your catchment area; then drystack your dirt until the storms come. You will put through far more ground than you could ever hope to do with a dry-blower.

Western Australia is the home of the dry-blower. It is used in northern Australia, and in Queensland too. But in the particularly dry areas of Westralia it has won many thousands of ounces of gold. The principle of the ingenious machine is to make a draught of air do most of the work that water does in a cradle.

The machine is a little complicated; so if you wish to make one, read carefully. Three that are practically perfect will here be described. They are the invention or series of inventions of Queenslanders after discarding other types of machines. These three machines did their work so well that they were investigated, described, and drawn to scale by an officer of the Queensland Mines Department, and you have here the benefit of his painstaking work. The drawings are to scale, so if you are handy with tools you cannot go astray. Choose any one of these machines you fancy. They proved wonderfully efficient on the Clermont field, and since that field's decline similar machines have done work wherever "dry gold" has been located. You can't use a dry-blower on clayey or moist ground. The drier the ground, the easier worked. You see, it "blows away."

There are three principles: (1) The separation of pebbles by a coarse perforated plate. (2) The delivery of the material passed through on to a finely-perforated screen. (3) Forcing through the fine screen a blast of air sufficiently strong to remove the dust and finer sands without blowing away the gold. The wind draught is obtained by a strong but ordinary bellows.

CARLSON'S DRY-BLOWER

Examine the illustrations. Both hopper and hopper-screen are on top of the machine. The wind-chest, zinc perforated screen, and riffle-box below are all fixed to the long board forming the top of the double bellows. As the handle attached to the bellows is raised or lowered to produce the blast, so the hopper, riffle-box, and wind-chest is rocked from side to side with a seesaw motion, the fulcrum being the block of wood separating the two bellows. The hopper-screen and its riffles are not removable and only require to be looked at occasionally for coarse gold. But the riffle-box, to which is attached the zinc screen, requires to be taken out frequently. This box has two sides tapering towards the front, so that it may be firmly wedged into a number of metal fastenings and set perfectly air-tight on the top of the wind-chest.

CARLSON'S DRY-BLOWER

Scale

0   1   2   3 FEET.

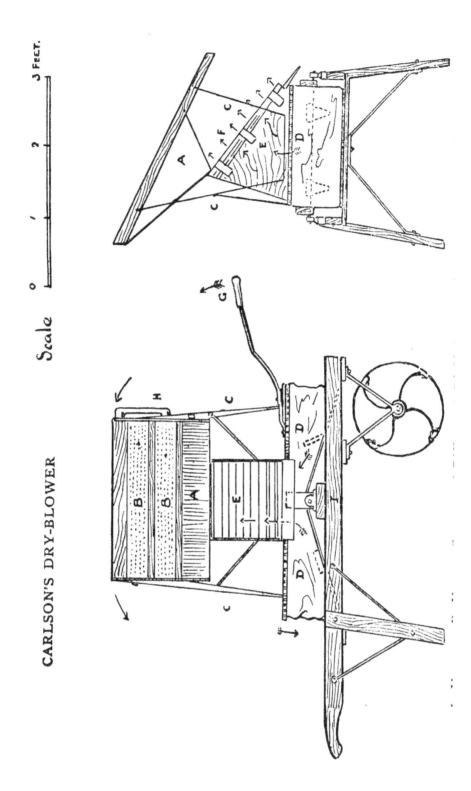

In operating the machine the coarse material comes over the front of the hopper, the finer portion being delivered on to the top of the riffle-box, where the seesaw motion and the pulsating blast together cause it either to be blown out or descend over the riffles. The residue in the riffle-box is thrown into the dish, then wind-blown by tossing or pouring it from one dish to another.

Now, this is a process about which you know nothing as yet. Practice makes perfect. It is on that age-old winnowing principle of throwing grain into the air to let the wind blow away the chaff. In cleaning your concentrates, the wind blows away the dust and finer sand; the heavy gold grains fall back into the dish.

The same result is gained by pouring the concentrates from one dish into the other, like pouring water. The gravel grains too heavy to "float" away are taken out with the fingers. The dry-blowers shake the dish, settling the gold exactly as you do when washing a prospect; only instead of allowing the water to lap away the top layer of sand, the dry-blower "peels" it off with his finger or thumb. Then he shakes the dish again, "settles" the gold, and again "thumb scrapes" the top sand off. Finally, he blows the concentrates with the mouth, and thus puffs the last sand away.

RANKINE'S DRY-BLOWER

In this machine there are two screens to the top of the hopper, one coarser than the other, each provided with riffles. The motion of hopper and top-screens is not the seesaw of Carlson's; this is horizontal, from side to side. The zinc screen and box are placed above a single bellows, both remain stationary during the operation of blowing. The handle is supported on a rigid iron frame acting as a fulcrum, connected by a bar to the hopper, while another bar extending along the back of the machine connects with the bellows. The hopper is supported on the side next to the handle by a swinging iron frame resting on the fixed iron frame supporting the handle, and on the other side the hopper is kept in position by two flat wooden supports attached to the base. These supports are slender and act as springs to pull the hopper back to a central position after the handle, when moved up or down, has forced it to either side.

BUHRE'S DRY-BLOWER

This machine combines the horizontal motion of the hopper and the stationary riffle-box of Rankine's Blower with the double bellows of Carlson's Blower. Some men declare they get better results from a "double blast" bellows than a single one. The bottom board of the double bellows is made the foundation of the machine, while the tops are hinged to the sides of the wind-chest. The handle moves the top of the bellows, which by a rod is connected to one side of the hopper. As the handle is moved upwards the air is drawn into the bellows on that side, and at the same time the connecting-rod forces the hopper to the right. Another connecting-rod from the other side of the hopper is attached to the opposite bellows, and as this is depressed a blast is driven up through the zinc screen.

A good point about this machine is that the hinges of the two bellows are placed on top instead of at the bottom. Difficulty is experienced in keeping the hinges free from accumulated dust when they are placed at the bottom as in Carlson's and Rankine's. The constant motion squeezes dust into crevices between the hinges, and these, sometimes, are strained or burst.

But, dry-blowers are "touchy" machines. If you have to use one, make it exact to measurements; otherwise it won't work.

Ground has to be perfectly dry to dry-blow. When it is dug, throw away all stones, break up clods, and generally flatten the dirt out. The finer it is the better it goes through and also the less chance of losing gold. The gold is not likely to blow away on its own, but any fine grain adhering to a speck of dirt will go when that speck is blown away.

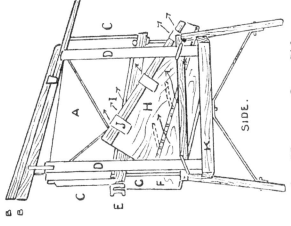

SIDE.

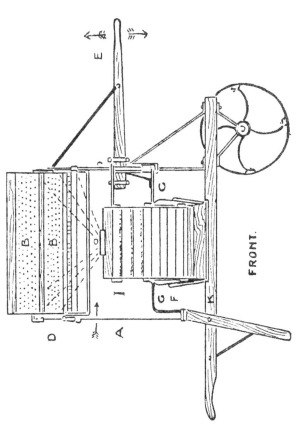

FRONT.

A. Hopper.   B. Hopper Screen and Riffles.   C. Iron Support for Hopper, One Side.
D. Wooden Springs.   E. Handle.   F. Single Bellows, Bottom Movable.   G. Bellows
Support.   H. Wind Chest and Valves.   I. Perforated Zinc Screen and Riffles.   G. Flange
for Fixing Screen in Position.   K. Barrow Frame

Make the perforations on the zinc screen an eighth of an inch apart in six parallel rows across the screen above each riffle. The riffles may be six or eight. Perforate with a blunt No. 8 sewing needle.

Fit well the riffle-box with the zinc screen, and make it air-tight. If you make a fan or a home-made bellows, as some men do, and your machine won't work, it is probably the fault of your bellows. The machine always works at its best when the blast is pulsating.

The hopper-screens are generally of galvanized iron and the perforations half an inch in diameter. Use seasoned timber. Green timber shrinks under the sun, naturally causing a leak in the wind-chest. With your machine built on a wheelbarrow framework, you can transport it anywhere.

Here is the South Australian dry-blower, for description and drawing of which I am obliged to the South Australian Mines Department:—

A light, portable framework supports an inclined screen-plate of punched sheet-iron, on which the roughly pulverized dirt is shovelled. A rocking movement imparted to this screen causes the fine material to fall through the holes, the coarse stones and gravel passing off as waste over the end of the screen. The fine material falls on to an apron-plate, which directs it on to the upper portion of a ripple-box, set on the top side of an 18 in. or 20 in. bellows. The ripple-box, which is the gold saving part of the appliance, is some 10 in. or 12 in. long by about 6 in. wide, and has a bottom of sacking or similar material supported on fine wire screen. This box has two or three small ripple- bars across it, and is fastened to, but is removable from, the top of the bellows. The nozzle of the bellows is removed and the opening closed, and a series of holes fitted with clacks or valves are made in the top of the bellows under the ripple-box. The bellows is so set in the main frame that its top and the attached ripple- box are inclined at a suitable angle.

In operation, the dirt passing through the screen falls on the top end of the ripple-box, and the working of the bellows causes puffs of air to come through the permeable bottom under the dirt, lifting it a little each time. The heavy particles of gold tend to settle down behind the ripples, but the lighter waste is thrown up a little by the puffs of air, and, helped by the inclination of the ripple-box, works forward and passes over the end, leaving the gold and heavy mineral particles behind the ripples in the box. At regular intervals the concentrate is removed and panned off to recover the gold. The shaking

BUHRE'S DRY-BLOWER

A. Hopper. B. Screen and Riffles. C. Hinged Hopper Supports. D. Double Bellows,
Top Movement. E. Handle for Right Hand. G. Wind Chest. H. Perforated Zinc
Screen and Riffles. I. Flanges Keeping Zinc Screen in Position

of the screen and the working of the bellows is controlled by one movement through suitable arms or levers. In the machine shown in the sketch plan, the movement of the screen is longitudinal, but in some designs the motion is sideways. These machines, when properly designed, are capable of saving fine gold, as well as coarse.

Now for a little about nuggetty ground. Such ground has been found in practically every Australian State. There is a mystery about nuggets. No one understands exactly where they come from. Some men say from reefs. Others believe from wet concentration, that is, from the drying up of mineral springs whose waters held gold in solution. Put a billy of sea-water on the fire and boil it away. Salt remains. That is the principle. Other men go so far as to say that "gold grows." Anyway, on some nuggetty fields, the nuggets may have rained from the sky, to all appearances.

Nuggets generally occur in "patches," in this instance patches of country. The actual area the nuggets cover may be only an acre or two, or a strip of country two miles long. The nuggets are scattered. In working nuggetty ground, you are either "on a nugget or nothing." It is unusual for fine gold to be associated with true nuggets.

Nuggets may be right on the surface. Generally they are a few inches under the loam with grass roots upon them. There is no method in seeking nuggets. Where they are, there they are. If you are in nuggetty ground, dig out the ground in a face. If there are nuggets in your ground, you will find them. If you are in "nuggetty country," and the ridges around are heavily impregnated with ironstone, then keep an eye on lumps of ironstone as you walk along. In such country, the gold is sometimes covered with a thin film of iron oxide, deposited in solution by rain-water. An iron-coated nugget lying right on the surface, shows that fascinating dull yellow underneath when turned over. On Ebagoolah, in Cape York Peninsula, 50 per cent of the gold found (apart from the reef gold) has been iron coated. Gold is still being found that was thrown away by the earlier diggers as ironstone.

If you scratch an ironstone pebble that is really gold, the yellow will show in the scratch. Sluicers in ironstone country often pick up a likely-looking ironstone pebble from the race, feel its weight, and bite it.

Nuggets also occur, of course, in creeks; but in such instances they have almost certainly come from reefs, and have a little quartz adhering to them. Numbers of mining fields have their "Nuggetty Gullies." Perhaps a field has twenty payable gullies and yet only one Nuggetty Gully. The other gullies carry gold from coarse down to fines. It's queer. Fields have been found where the creeks carried ordinary shorty gold, while later on nuggets were found away up on the bare ridges. You can figure it out yourself as to how the heavier metal got up there instead of tumbling down into the creeks. You will have many a guess coming. Gold is "queer." Do you know that if you place grains of fine gold under a cube of lead, then put a glass case over the cube and leave it alone for a couple of years, the gold will work right up through the lead!

I don't suggest that that is the way in which the nuggets climbed the hill, but the illustration will make you realize that there are many things about gold which we do not know.

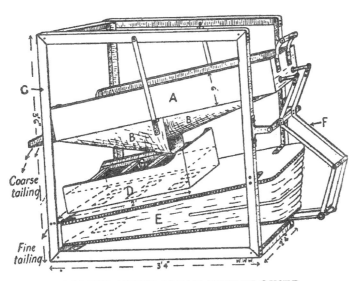

SOUTH AUSTRALIAN DRY-BLOWER

A. Shaking screen. B. Metal chutes delivering on to C. C. Removable porous tray with ripples and bottom of hessian or towelling backed by metal gauze. D. Wind box. E. Bellows with clack valves opening into D and with trap below to facilitate removal of dust. F. Gearing which operates bellows while shaking screen is pushed to and fro. G. Anglo-iron frame.

The only known method to locate nuggets (most elusive of the gold family) is to find a probable locality and then get into the ground with pick and shovel and elbow grease.

Remember above all, if you have reason to believe that nuggets may exist in a certain area of ground, look around first and see if you can get water on to that ground, then hand sluice it. It will save you untold labour and time. Besides, if there is any fine gold in that ground you will get it, instead of throwing it away with the shovel.

FLUMING HEAD-RACE WATER ACROSS GORGE

XIX

Prospecting for Reefs

Reef-mining is quite different to alluvial. A reef is a line of stone often showing above the surface. It comes straight up out of the earth, or runs down, which ever term you prefer, to any depth, maybe only 100 feet in depth, maybe 2000. Perhaps it "runs" straight, perhaps it slopes (inclines) at a sharp angle. The gold is in the stone. The stone is crushed by battery and the gold extracted. Don't be alarmed by a battery. You will soon have a battery if you locate a payable reef. If you are a "leader-chaser" you will crush your own stone with a "Spring Dolly," a simple contrivance. A "leader" is a small reef, say, up to eighteen inches wide. Some leader-chasers are aristocrats. They will only chase "specimen" leaders. A specimen leader is one in which the stone makes rich patches of specimen gold. The "chasers" dolly the specimens in a hand dolly-pot and leave the rest of the leader (it may still contain good battery stone) to any who come after.

Stone going one ounce to the ton as a rule is payable providing the reef is handy to a battery, and the gold does not carry silver or other impurities: also providing you have not to put on machinery to cope with water.

The reefs you will be mainly interested in are quartz. You will see the old white stone very likely on your first day out. Quartz of course can be any colour under the sun. Always examine ironstone reefs as well as quartz. Ironstone, quartz, and gold are often found together. In fact a quartz reef without some ironstone in it is a rare exception. Honeycombed ironstone, its cavities filled with yellow brown oxide of iron, is always worth dollying.

While prospecting for alluvial you will naturally be on the lookout for reefs too. If your dish prospects show ragged gold with sharp edges, or if you are getting an odd little specimen in your dish, and if your colours are not at all waterworn, you are straight away on the lookout for the reef that probably is shedding this sharp edged gold. You need the barest addition to your tools. A hammer-headed pick is handy for reef-chasing. Get a light pick that won't remind you all day of its weight. You can root out a prospect anywhere with that pick. Its hammer head is for cracking stones. You need a dolly-pot at the camp, half of an old iron mercury bottle is the usual dolly. There are generally plenty around old mining-camps. For a pestle, use a light discarded hammer-headed pick, or short length of bar iron, anything that will crush your stone (your sample).

A sample is the fragment of stone you knock from a likely looking reef. For testing purposes, it is not necessary to pound up more than two or three ounces. Please yourself. Most beginners dolly up pounds weight of stone unnecessarily. Pound and grind the sample fairly fine, then tip it into the dish giving the bottom of the dolly-pot a bang with the pestle as you do so. The bang will loosen any specks of free gold which may be adhering to the bottom of the pot. Wash your "crushings" as you would an alluvial sample. If you are dollying good stone, always clean your dolly when you have finished those particular samples. Otherwise, the next sample you dolly may be a duffer showing a false prospect from the colours of gold left in the dolly. Such a false prospect may cause you much fruitless work, and disappointment.

A universal "dish" for the reef prospector is one of those tiny frying-pans with the handle cut off. The prospector comes back to camp after a morning's cruise in the hills, throws his bag of specimens on the ground, puts on the billy, has "kai-kai," then brings up a dishful of water from the creek. He squats comfortably with the dolly-pot between his legs and puts through the samples, using the wee frying-pan as a dish and the dish as the creek.

In a morning's or a day's walk among the hills you may collect numerous samples. Don't mix them, or lose your locality; good "shows" have been lost that way and never re-located. Carry your samples in a sugar-bag or make a special bag. One like a long sleeve is the best, with pieces of string sewn every ten inches or so up the sleeve. Drop in your sample and tie the string. Do the same with succeeding samples and they are never mixed. The "sleeve" bag is also very handy to carry. Loop it over the shoulder and under the arm like a bandolier.

Memorize the locality of every reef from which you took a sample, so that you can go straight back to the spot if the sample dollies gold. Picture in your mind a tall white tree standing up on the ridge, or any landmark which takes your eye or fancy. And don't forget in which direction your camp lies, either.

With a little experience, you will begin to distinguish between "likely stone" and "buck" reefs, quartzite, etc. This chapter is not to teach you reef-mining: a big book would be needed for that. Here you will find valuable knowledge in prospecting for, and the proved methods employed in locating, payable reefs. Should you find such a reef, you will soon learn how to work it or sell it. Advise the Mines Department if you locate a gold-bearing reef and are in doubt how next to proceed.

As when prospecting for alluvial, try all gullies, particularly the heads of gullies, and, more important still, those little half-formed ravines that lead into the heads of gullies. An auriferous reef, with its cap exposed on the side of a mountain, spur, ridge, or hill, sheds gold. Naturally it sheds downhill. Naturally also, when the rains come they wash some particles of gold and light specimens downhill into the nearest rivulet among the grass roots, and from there in the course of time carry the colours into those faint gutters that run farther down into the hollows that soon form the branch heads of ravines. The cap of a reef may be plainly visible on the surface, with gold showing in the stone. On the other hand, it may be fully or partly covered by earth, grass, timber, logs, ferns, undergrowth, leaves and the debris of the bush. Seek, and you may find. Many a man has walked over and missed a fortune by not keeping his eyes open and his wits awake.

So, if your dish shows you a prospect of gold in a gully, follow it up. If the prospects carry right on up the gully to its head, then try every branch gully that leads into the head. Soon you will locate the branch gully down which the gold is coming to the main gully. Follow the branch gully up, dishing every thirty feet or so, every hundred yards or more if you are on a good "trail." If you trace the gold right to the head of the branch gully, then try the tiny ravines that lead into it: locate your traces again and follow them right up until the ravine fades out on the side of the hill. Then look above you carefully. You will see numerous tiny dry rivulets, perhaps covered by grass. Visualize a heavy storm with the water pouring down the hill into your ravine. Very quickly you will see a dozen "gutters" down which the water would flow into the ravine. Try all these gutters until you strike the colours again. Follow them up while they last. Very likely they will guide you right to the cap of the reef. If not lie flat where you took the last colour prospect: gaze up the hill or along its crown as the case may be: see where the ground ahead of you has the gentlest, even the faintest slope. Try right there. Remember water must run downward; and water was responsible for laying that thin trail of perhaps "powder" gold that you are following.

Of course, if you see as you work up a hill or slope an outcrop of stone away ahead of you, go and "knap" it (break pieces off) for that quite possibly may be the reef which has shed the colours.

If your colours appear to have "faded" out, or if you are on a long gentle hillslope a long way from water, try "loaming." Make a long narrow bag, a huge "sock" similar to that you made for your sample stone, with strings attached to keep each loaming separate. From where you last got colours, take a prospect (a quarter of a dish) every thirty feet or so right away ahead, on the surface, among the grass roots or rubble. When your loaming bag is filled with prospects carry them to the creek and wash them. You know exactly where you got the loamings. The first sample is No. 1: there is the spot in the ground from where you got No. 1 loaming, etc.

If you have not located the reef, and can find no more prospects, come back to where you got the last prospect and start a narrow trench right up the hill. You won't have to go far for bottom, in this case the solid rock that forms the hill. Numbers of men in trenching, should the bottom be a few feet deep, make their bottom the harder ground just under the loam. But you will be surer if you go to real bottom. That may be only three or four inches, seldom more than three or four feet down. When you are on the crown of a hill, or any bare hillslope, your bottom possibly will be a matter of inches only. Often you can scrape up your prospects with the shovel blade, then clean out the cracks with a twig. Glance around for any tiny dry rivulet, often they look like "ant tracks" filled with wee pebbles of iron-stone. Take a prospect from such a dry rivulet. It is a fine catch for any gold that may have been shed from a reef close by. Very possibly you may get some miniature ironstone specimens in that tiny depression.

You are now "trenching," that is, trying to "cut" the reef. If it runs anywhere on the hill-side crosswise to you, then you must eventually cut it. As you trench, you will very likely strike quite a number of leaders or reefs. Don't be surprised or disheartened if they are "duffers." Not every reef, by a long way, carries gold. Keep on until you find your golden reef, or until it has you beaten. Gold is a funny thing. Sometimes it beats the keenest prospector. Because you find a trail of reef gold, that does not say you are certain to locate the reef. But you have a very favourable chance.

As you cut on with the trench, you may strike a reef that carries gold. Don't throw your shovel in the air and yell that you are made. Turn the trench along that reef, then break up its "cap" (the stone above surface or bottom) and see if there is more gold. That reef may not be payable. Some reefs only carry a speck or two of gold here and there.

Should you run your trench right "out" and not locate the reef, come back to where you got your last loam prospect and trench at right-angles to the first trench. That reef may run parallel to the trench already cut.

Prospecting for a tin reef is exactly the same as for gold. However, if you are in tin country, and you get on the trace of a reef, you will probably locate that reef much quicker than if it had been gold. This, because a tin reef contains a vastly greater quantity of tin than a gold reef does of gold. There may be tons of tin specimens lying upon the surface around a tin reef. Much tin is shed as surface alluvial. The rains wash this down into the ravines, gullies, and creeks often in quantities of hundredweights, sometimes in tons, and scatter tell-tale traces over a far greater area than a gold reef would do.

Remember, tin is a very good proposition. As it occurs in practically the same class of country as gold (that is, it occurs generally in granite and slate country and in deep leads under basalt, which is near enough for you) always keep a look out for it. Wolfram also occurs, and is prospected for, much in the same way. Bismuth and scheelite, much rarer metals and very valuable, though the prices fluctuate, are at times closely associated with tin country. If you pick up a specimen of either, it will feel its weight in lead.

But describing minerals other than gold and tin is beyond the scope of this book, and, besides, you might get confused. One hint only: always examine any particularly heavy stone.

The Mines Department will willingly assay any sample you may send them—post them down say a pound weight of the stone.

XX

Reefing

When trenching for a reef, carry up a dish of water and leave it beside the trench. Then when you cut a likely-looking stone, dolly a sample and try it with your frying-pan. You can wash a hundred dolly prospects in the one dish of water, and are thus saved a hundred trips down to the creek. You often get a "line" on the "class" of stone in your reef in that way, for reefs invariably shed "floaters." A floater is a piece of stone which has broken from a reef and either fallen, been washed away, or blown away. Thus, if you unearth a floater and it has visible gold, or dollies to a decent prospect, you know the sort of stone to look for. If your floater is milky quartz intersected by "blue veins," the reef will, probably, be the same class of stone. So that if, immediately afterwards, you cut a "glassy" reef you do not waste over much time prospecting it, but carry on with the trench searching for the reef which shed the floater.

Floaters are often picked up on the surface, away down the hill-side. They may be hundreds of yards or only a few feet away from the reef. If you pick up a floater, walk up the hill scanning the ground for others. Knap every likely-looking stone you see. You may get a "line" of floaters leading right to the reef. You "speck" those floaters, odd ones may be lying fully exposed on the surface, others may have only a point showing from under a tuft of grass. You must walk very slowly, using your eyes, and swing the pick on any stone that just shows from the ground.

Should you pick up a floater in a gully, there may be a chase ahead of you. That floater may have rolled down a hill, and, after many floods, been washed for miles. Well, examine it. Is the stone waterworn? If so, how much so? Estimate how far it has probably travelled and whether it is worth the trouble of following up. In any case, prospect that gully very thoroughly. You may not only find other floaters, but also specimens and alluvial. Reefs shed much alluvial gold. The presence of floaters proves that reefs are in the vicinity. A gully will often carry the floaters from a number of reefs.

A floater may lead you on to a "Specimen Gully." Many hundreds of specimen gullies have been found in Australia. Often the reef is never found. Probably it is all in the gully, denuded and washed there as specimens and alluvial. Do not bother about wash if prospecting for reefs. Try any ravine, no matter how bare or sprinkled with surface stones the bottom may be. The tiny ledges and crevices in a bare ravine bottom are the "catches" for reef prospects. Alluvial from reefs is generally very jagged, often with tiny particles of quartz adhering. It contains little specimens too. The more jagged, the rougher, the less waterworn the prospect is, the nearer the reef.

If you haven't a dolly-pot, a jam- or milk-tin makes an excellent one, until it wears out. Clean it well, and stand it on a solid bottom—the axe-blade if you haven't an anvil.

A Spring Dolly is a very slow, old-time method of crushing your own stone; but it is effective if the stone is rich. Here is how to make one: find the springiest-looking sapling you can. Fall it, and set it up close to your stone. Plant it very firmly in the ground. Hitch a rope or chain to the top, and to the end of the chain a "Stamper"—a heavy log similar to that cut for a windlass barrel. To the dropping end of the stamper, attach a flat iron "shoe." A few inches up from it, bore a hole and shove a projecting stick through. In operation, grasp this handle with both hands, one on each side of the stamper.

With the weight of the stamper, the sapling bends a certain degree. Directly under the stamper shoe is a stump, or you put in a post. Chisel the top out box shape. About eight inches down leave a rim, upon which you lay very short iron bars, a fraction of an inch apart. Under these bars the stump is still hollow. By your feet is an outlet through which the crushed stone falls.

Put a handful of stone on the bars, grasp the stamper handle, and pull it down. She comes with a bang and leaps up, taking your nose with it if you are not careful. Part of the stone is crushed and slips down through the bars.

After some days of laborious work, your little heap of stone is "through." Perhaps you have to sieve it then. The "fines are ready for the box but you may have to crush the coarse again. It is a slow process, and loses some of the gold. Still, it's handy should you locate a reef which carries only a few tons of payable stone, and you need a few pounds to pay the storekeeper. If you find a reef rich enough to hand-dolly, it certainly is rich enough for a battery.

In reefing country especially, always try any patches of rubble that you see on the surface or down a hillside. Reef stone is invariably flat stone. The general colour is from white to brown but reefing stone can be practically any colour under the sun. Many stones oxidize, weather and sun stain them. A lump of quartz milky white inside may be almost black on the outside. Examine any landslide or fall of a bank. These sometimes expose leaders. Keep an eye open when walking up creeks and gullies. Reefs are often exposed there. A creek is really a giant trench where Nature has worked for you; she has literally sluiced out that "trench," and a reef may be there ready exposed if you have the eyes to see. Examine any "blow," especially if quartz or iron-stone is among it. A blow appears like an upheaval of rock. Unlike a reef, it does not run in a thin, well defined line.

"Leader-chasers" confine their attention mostly to the location of small rich leaders. A leader may be from a quarter-inch thick to nine inches. Some men have an uncanny instinct for locating payable leaders. They "smell" them out. A leader is generally shallow in depth, perhaps only twenty feet; but a well-defined leader may go down a hundred feet. That is unusual.

Remember, these men who "smell out" leaders do it by exactly the same process that I am describing. They use their eyes, their wits, the pick and dish. They never get disheartened. They know that if they do not find a payable leader today, they will to-morrow or some other morrow.

They don't get tired. They just keep good humoured and keep on trying.

In good leader country, some leaders may carry phenomenally rich patches of specimen stone.

Perhaps the gold (as often in a reef) is contained in a "chute," or lense. That is, the gold does not occur evenly throughout the stone, but goes straight down in one spot. A chute may be three feet in length along any part of the reef or leader. It probably will be the width of the reef, and possibly go straight down to any depth at which it cuts out. Sometimes chutes gradually taper out: sometimes the gold thins to a thread which carries on for feet to make into a rich patch of stone again: sometimes the gold contents vanish abruptly. A chute may be on an inclined plane, and a reef which has a chute may carry gold only in that chute. Therefore, if you knap a likely-looking reef and get no prospect, try along its outcropping line; otherwise you may possibly miss a chute.

Reef and leader gold is invariably "patchy." Some reefs "average," that is the gold is throughout the reef stone. But such reefs are unusual. They occur much more frequently in huge poor propositions than in smaller reefs. A patch of golden stone may "make" anywhere at all in a reef. Often you know nothing about it until your pick "breaks" gold. Some reefs have "indicators." A trail of a particular kind of stone which only occurs with the gold in that reef, will lead right up to the gold. Indicators have various peculiarities. Perhaps a streak of ironstone leads to golden stone: perhaps the "formation" along the side of the reef has a queer characteristic of turning a deep choc-olate green, feet or yards away from the gold: perhaps gold can be expected to "make" when the reef shows indications of "bulging." Not every reef has its queer little individual "indicator." When men find such a reef they soon distinguish its particular indicator and are always on the lookout for it when sinking or driving in search of another patch.

Reefs and leaders may possess more than one chute or patch. Where two reefs intersect, or where a leader runs into a reef, and especially when either leader or reef carries a little gold, the line of intersection is where, almost certainly, gold may "make." A reef may "make" gold when it strikes a change of country. If you are working a reef, and the dolly pot shows gold at all, then follow that stone. It may "make" at any time. Remember, when you are reefing, your dolly-pot is your "dish." Try a dolly prospect of the reef now and again, especially if the stone changes.

In leader country, a hill may be a network of leaders. A trench a hundred feet long may cut twenty or more leaders. Odd ones may carry gold. If so, in such a hill there will be innumerable little "caps" jutting above the surface, patches of rubble everywhere, plenty of wee specimens, and the surface will always give indications to the dish.

The tools for working a reef include half a dozen drills, several hammers, a light forge (ordinary household bellows) and the usual tools of the alluvial digger.

Battery charges are usually £1 per ton. So if you locate a reef, you must estimate its value per ton of stone, allowing for the time you spend in bringing each ton to the surface. Then deduct £1 per ton battery charge, and 10s. more or less (depending on distance) for carting. Then, if your gold is worth £3 8s. per oz. you know, approximately, whether the reef is worth working. The only sure method is to sink down on the best stone, take out a crushing say of ten tons and put it through the nearest battery. Then you know where you are.

Of course, if you strike a golden reef your troubles of a lifetime will be over. All you will have to do is bag the "jeweller's shop" at your feet. But there are many reefs highly payable apart from a "golden reef."

Some reef-chasers find a small pocket magnifying glass handy. Not many men carry them. If you crack a stone and cannot see gold in it with the naked eye, that particular sample is, generally, not worthwhile dollying. There are exceptions, and it is these exceptions that keep you busy with the dolly. I have seen stone going ten ounces to the ton (rich stone) the gold in which was so fine, and in other cases was so discoloured by iron, as to be quite invisible to the naked eye. For the beginner, a magnifying glass would be handy, he could much more readily distinguish a tiny speck of gold in discoloured stone. It would be handier still in proving that "all is not gold that glitters." With a glass, you can detect lots of "yellow stuff" that appears to be gold but is not. A magnifying glass is more frequently used by prospectors to whom "all is fish that comes into the net." There are other valuable minerals besides gold.

A last hint on reefing and leader-chasing. This may save you much work, time and heartbreak. If you are prospecting a gully and nearly jump from your skin at sight of a fat, shiny, seven weight piece in the dish, don't yell that you are made. The gold may be only from a "mullocky leader." Some mullocky leaders will yield a hundred ounces in a week, and then cut out. Some may not yield five ounces.

Look at your prospect after the first transports are over. Is a strip of hard red stuff like rust, or burnt clay, or friable ironstone adhering to it? If so, you may often safely say: "Mullocky leader. Now where is it?"

Try right up the creek or gully to make sure that you really are not on a new alluvial patch. Then come back and trace that mullocky gold up the creek until it cuts out. Then search the banks on either side. You may find the leader, not half an inch wide, in the clayey or loamy creek-bank. It will very likely "cut out" immediately the ground gets hard.

XXI

Erecting a Battery

When you get your stone you must crush it. If a State or private battery is not handy, circumstances may force you to erect your own. Don't attempt to do so, if you are a new hand at the game, unless a Mines Department man assures you that your reef is payable. Any battery man will show you how to drive a battery in "a day's run." It is in the repair work, in amalgamating the plates and cleaning up, that experience must be learned.

In the following description, don't be frightened if some of the terms sound like "machinery." Many men can drive a motor-car, but few men know their "innards." A battery is much simpler than a motor-car.

A five-head stamper battery will interest you most. Briefly, the stone is crushed in an iron mortar box, in the bottom of which are placed five stamper dies, generally, of forged steel. On to these drop the stamper shoes of manganese steel. Each shoe has a shank, the top of which fits into the socket of the head; and this is permanently fitted to the stamper stem. Each stem has a cross-keyed tappet that can be easily shifted to alter the drop and take up the wear of the shoes.

These five stampers are supported vertically by a wooden framework carrying guides. A horizontal shaft carries five cams, which as the shaft rotates catch under the tappets, which in turn lift the stampers. As the shaft turns round, the stampers fall. The quartz in the mortar box is thus crushed between the stamper shoes and dies. The battery is worked by a steam or oil engine, by means of belting on a pulley rotating a counter shaft. The pinion on this shaft fits into a spur-wheel on the end of the cam-shaft.

The stone is fed into the mortar box by shovel, or a chute so fixed that the vibration of the battery automatically shakes the quantity required into the mortar box. A slow stream of water, regulated by a tap, is turned on from the storage tank. As the stone is crushed, the stampers, in falling, force the muddy water against a mesh screen in front of the mortar box. Thus, as slimes, the stone passes through the screen and flows over wooden tables on which are copper plates coated with quicksilver. Quicksilver has an affinity for gold and catches the finely crushed particles as the sands and slimes flow over the plates. A little experience will show you how simple the process is.

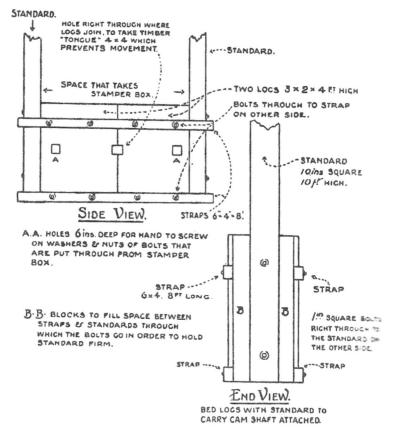

SIDE VIEW.

STANDARD.

HOLE RIGHT THROUGH WHERE LOGS JOIN, TO TAKE TIMBER "TONGUE" 4 × 4 WHICH PREVENTS MOVEMENT.

STANDARD.

SPACE THAT TAKES STAMPER BOX.

TWO LOGS 3 × 2 × 4 FT HIGH

BOLTS THROUGH TO STRAP ON OTHER SIDE.

STANDARD 10 ins SQUARE 10 ft HIGH.

STRAPS 6"× 4"× 8'.

A.A. HOLES 6 ins. DEEP FOR HAND TO SCREW ON WASHERS & NUTS OF BOLTS THAT ARE PUT THROUGH FROM STAMPER BOX.

STRAP 6 × 4. 8 FT LONG.

STRAP

B·B· BLOCKS TO FILL SPACE BETWEEN STRAPS & STANDARDS THROUGH WHICH THE BOLTS GO IN ORDER TO HOLD STANDARD FIRM.

1 IN SQUARE BOLTS RIGHT THROUGH TO THE STANDARD ON THE OTHER SIDE.

STRAP

STRAP

END VIEW.
BED LOGS WITH STANDARD TO CARRY CAM SHAFT ATTACHED.

ERECTING A BATTERY

Now, as you and your mates may wish to erect your own battery, I will explain how my old mate, Lige Henderson, recently erected his five modern head out Coramba way. Lige has been mining and driving his own battery single-handed for twenty years. So what one man can do, surely you and your mates can do.

Your battery site should be fifteen or twenty feet above your water-supply. Later on you may want to put concentrators under your tables. Quite likely you will want to save the tailings until you become ambitious enough to erect cyanide vats for tailings treatment. With your battery erected, say, twenty feet above the creek, you will have room for later additions. Choose, if possible, hard ground for the battery "bed." Concrete, of course, is the ideal bed. However, choose hard ground, and make your bed plate of blue gum or spotted gum logs. Failing these, any hardwood.

Two bed-logs are required, three feet by two feet by four inches. Before bedding, fit them together and mark so that a square hole can be cut, half in each log so that when put together a four-inch square piece of timber can be fitted into the hole.

Lay both logs down together, and at the bottom and along the whole breadth cut out a piece two inches deep by six inches wide. Cut out another piece of the same size along the whole breadth of the logs one foot from the top. (The top line of the cut should be one foot from the top of the logs.) Turn the logs over and do exactly the same on the other side. These cuts are to take 6x4 timber, which being eight feet long will project a foot at each end of the log. We will call these eight-feet lengths of timber "straps." Put the straps into the grooves cut for them. Bore four holes in the bottom strap right through to the bottom strap on the other side—two holes to each log. These holes are to take inch bolts threaded at both ends. Bore four similar holes in the top strap. Next, bolt through to top and bottom straps on the other side, put on washers and nuts and screw up securely from both sides. Now you have your logs bolted firmly together. Select a tough piece of 4 x 4 timber and drive it through the square hole that you have cut in the centre of the logs. This is the "tongue" that prevents movement.

Turn your logs up on end—they are now all one piece—and, at the ends where the standards to hold the cam-shaft are to be placed, bore a hole a foot from the bottom right through to the other end. Then bore another hole a foot from the top. These holes are to take an inch bolt eight feet long and threaded at both ends. The bolts will be long enough to go through the standards when they are put on.

Next see that the log is trimmed true on top. Make a template of the bottom of the mortar box place it on the block; mark the four holes for the holding down bolts which are inch-and-a-quarter bolts, threaded at both ends. Next, cut chambers in the sides of your log two feet down to meet the bolt holes, so that when the bolts are put in you can place your hand in the chamber and put the nut and washer on the end of each bolt.

A few paragraphs back it was said that the straps would project a foot at each end. Between these projections you place your standards, with blocks of wood running the length of the log to fill in the space between the standard and the projections. Bore holes for bolts through the projections, the blocks, and the standard—these bolts will give added firmness to the standards which are ten-inch-square hardwood, ten feet high.

You understand that your bed-log is three feet in the ground, with a foot of timber above. If at that depth the bed-plate does not rest on solid ground, dig until it will. In that case, make the bed-plate logs longer but with otherwise the same measurements.

Remember the weight of the mortar box is twenty-one hundredweight. Bolt the brackets that carry the cam-shaft on to the standards. The cam-shaft is eight feet long, and three and a half inches in diameter: the bearings that it runs in are gun-metal lined. This shaft carries the five steel cams and a three-foot spur-wheel. The weight of shaft and cams including the spur-wheel is ten hundredweight. Each cam is keyed tightly to the shaft about three-quarters of an inch from the stamper stem.

Such is the main job in erecting a battery. I cannot mention every nut and bolt} there are not many of them, and it is not necessary for you to know the whole business from A to Z. The foregoing instructions and explanations are simply a guide. With them and the illustrations, plus a little elbow-grease and brains, you will soon erect your battery.

The guides are of tallowwood (or any hardwood) seven by six inches, made in halves. These guides take the stamper stems. The stems are two and three-quarter inches in diameter, and, including the heads and shoes, are ten feet six inches long. Each stamper-head is eight and a half inches in diameter by twelve inches, each shoe is eight and a half by eight inches.

Each tappet is cross-keyed, of cast-iron, steel faced. All steel is best. The tappet fits on the stamper stem: as the cam-shaft goes round, the cams come under the tappet lifting the stamper and dropping it as they pass. Each stamper (inclusive of tappet, head, and shoe) is five and a half hundredweight. The spur gear, pulley and bearings for the battery total seven and a half hundredweight. Each die weighs sixty pounds.

Now, you put a few inches of broken quartz in the bottom of the mortar box, enough to bring your dies up level with the discharge opening; then put in the dies and ram small quartz around them; otherwise they are liable to move with the pounding of the stampers, thus "flowering" the "silver," sliming the amalgam, and playing hell generally. The mortar box is four feet by one foot, three feet eight inches high. The discharge opening is three feet six indies by twelve inches. That opening is cut, of course out of the front of the box. A screen is fitted across it. This screen is woven steel wire, four hundred holes to the square inch. Tack it on to a wooden frame and place it in the opening. Use five seven-eighths of an inch screwed studs with clips and nuts on them. This makes a tight job and when removing the screen it is only necessary to loosen the nuts and turn the clip upside down. Through this screen the sands and slimes splash out on to the plates. Fit the splash-plate, four feet by eight inches wide on to the lip of the box: it will catch a good deal of your amalgam. The front of the box is covered by a wrought-iron splash-plate, otherwise the sands forced through the screen would fly across the plates and be lost.

In front of the screen is fitted the table seven feet by four feet, which carries two copper plates each two feet by four feet. Running across the top of the table just above the top plate is a shallow "well," four inches wide and three-quarters of an inch deep. A similar well (a gutter really) runs midway between the plates. These wells are to catch any splashes of quicksilver which have been forced through the screen and not caught by the plates.

The wooden tables, over which the sands flow, are to catch any amalgam that comes through the screen. Their purpose is the same as that part of your sluice race in which you save your gold. This table, too, must have a slight "fall." It is so made that it can be adjusted to any fall or pitch you require, by raising or lowering the "tail" of the table until your sands are gently rippling over the plates. At the foot of the table there is a deep well six inches deep and the same width. This catches anything that gets over the plates. There is room on the table for a third plate in case you have very fine, light gold. The contents of the deep well flow on to the blanket table, which is the same width as the plate table, but has a little more fall. It is best to use corduroy on this: it concentrates any heavy sands—mineralized sands which possibly contain gold in chemical combination with other minerals and has thus escaped amalgamation over the plates. Before starting crushing, drop some quicksilver in the mortar box: the amount depends on your estimation of the richness of stone per ton. Say you start work in the morning; you estimate you will put through three tons of stone in the day, and the stone will go two ounces to the ton, according to your dolly-pot prospects. Well, drop a "bead" of "silver" about half an inch wide into the mortar box.

As the stone is being crushed, this silver "grabs" any free gold it comes in contact with and forms amalgam, which stays within the box.

Again, throughout the day, a further small "bead" of "silver" must be dropped in at the back of the box every twenty minutes, the size of the bead again depending on the richness of the stone. For two-ounce stone, the bead should be a quarter of an inch.

This bead being always fresh and "lively" helps the silver already in the box and fastens on to the fresh particles of gold constantly being pounded out of the stone by the descending stampers. If you see silver dribbling down the plates, you are using too much: if the amalgam is hard and dry, you are not putting enough silver in the box. Dust a little silver on the plates when you are dressing them if they are dry. You easily regulate by tap the water running into the mortar box. Don't use too much water—just sufficient to cause the tailings to gently "wave" across the plates.

XXII

Amalgamation

Dressing the Plates: Crushing Stone

Now, we will still carry on with this battery. The fact that it is being success-fully used to-day by one of the most experienced reef-miners in New South Wales may give you more interest and confidence in this description.

Dressing the Plates.—Your battery plates are most important. The miner who works this battery, although constantly handling grease and engine oils, never lets any grease get near the battery plates or mortar box. Apply the same rule to your battery. Grease is the enemy of successful amalgamation. Always wash your hands thoroughly before dressing the plates. Don't kneel on the tables with grease spots on your knees. Always have a board to kneel on. Don't spit tobacco juice on the plates either. If you are a married man, don't let the children play jazz on the plates.

If your plates are new copper sheets, lay them on the tables, boil a bucket of water, sprinkle fine clean sand or tailings on the plates, then with a clean scrubbing-brush scrub the surface to be silvered. Burnish the copper if you like. The only grease you must put into those plates is elbow-grease. Next, sprinkle the plates with tailings. Have handy a small bottle half filled with quick-silver and tightly corked. Bore an one-eighth inch hole through the cork and sprinkle some "silver" in amongst the tailings on the plates. Now, get a lump of potassium cyanide, wrap it in a piece of damp flannel, and rub the ball so formed over the plates. It is a steady job, but not a long one if you have previously thoroughly cleaned the plates. This operation rubs the silver into them—it silvers the plates, that is, it forms the *amalgam* on them. We won't go into scientific explanations.

Remember potassium cyanide is one of the deadliest poisons known to science. If the fowls drink any cyanide water from the battery, they won't lay any more eggs. If children play about the battery where that water is, there may be a funeral. Always wash your hands carefully after using cyanide or anything that has touched it and keep your cyanide under lock and key.

Your plates now shine with silver like a highly polished mirror. Throw buckets of water on the plates to wash the sand and cyanide off. When not using your plates keep them covered with damp bags: this keeps them from oxidizing and the silver from evaporating. Remember to shoo the fowls and pup away.

If your hands were greasy, you will not have made a perfect job of it.

Now, especially if your plates are new, you must dress them occasionally while crushing. As soon as the oxide shows, they should be rubbed up. The amalgam must always be kept "lively." If it becomes "sick" it won't catch the fine gold passing over it. So, get a pickle-bottle, clean it thoroughly, make a tight wooden stopper, and bore, say, a half- inch hole through the centre of it. Fill the bottle with water, place the stopper in tightly, and force two small pieces of cyanide through the hole. They will soon dissolve. Next, get a clean enamel bucket and a flannel hand-rag. Always keep the same bucket for this job. After crushing a while, you will notice the plates are showing oxide and discolouring. Stop the battery. Sprinkle some of the cyanide water from the pickle-bottle on to the plates and rub it with the flannel all over them, finishing the job by "sweeping" up towards the top of each plate. Then throw water over them to wash away the cyanide. Always turn the water off at the box when you are doing this job.

Crushing Stone.—The plates now will be bright and lively again. Start the old engine and hear the stampers drop again with a joyous clatter. You know now the plates are doing their job, saving the fine gold as the slurry of sand and slime from the screen takes it over their bright faces.

Always keep your eye on the plates while the battery is running. If the sands are running over the plates too quickly just turn off the water a little. If the plates are "silting," turn on the water a little. Don't have too much pitch on the table—an inch and a quarter to the foot should do. If you have too much pitch the plates will scour. Perhaps your screen has "choked." Well, brush it with a steel-wire brush, so opening the tiny clogged holes.

Don't feed the battery too heavily. If you get too much stone under the stampers it will slow down the discharge and there is a danger of bursting your screen off. Only an inch or two of stone constantly between the stampers and the dies is needed. Should you notice little beads of quicksilver running over the plates, then the larger bead you drop every twenty minutes into the mortar box is too much. Put in less next time. If there is not enough gold in the stone to be taken up by the quicksilver, then you are wasting expensive "silver" by putting in too much. On the other hand, the stone may be richer than you anticipate and you are not putting in enough "silver." It is better to use too little than too much. When there is too much in the box and not enough gold to take it up, the stampers batter the "silver" about and cause it to flower, that is, go into minute particles which will flow over the plates and get away with the tailings. Remember when you are losing quicksilver in any form that has been in the box, you are losing gold also.

You can use "blanket" tables too with this battery if you wish. Put these tables directly behind the silvered plates. The blanket is a good idea for catching concentrates; but corduroy cloth is much superior to blankets. Use the cloth with the grooves crossways to the running sands. There is nothing like this cloth for saving concentrates and any "flowered" quicksilver that may have escaped over the plates. Wash these blankets fairly frequently, but don't wring them too tightly.

Concentrates, as you know, are heavy sands containing gold which has escaped amalgamation. You bag these concentrates. After many crushings, when you have collected a ton of concentrates, if you are not experienced enough to free them of gold by acids or other processes, send them to one of the city plants that treat such concentrates. The cost is not much and your concentrates may be valuable. Find their value by burning and grinding. It is a good idea to confirm by assay with the firm to whom you are going to consign them. Thus you know values beforehand, and do not pay carriage on worthless sand.

In this battery, no quicksilver is used in the wells across the tables. The wells are simply to catch anything that dribbles down the plates.

The screen in front of the mortar box has 400 holes to the square inch woven. Another screen has been tried with 240 punched holes to the square inch. Both these screens discharge to the same fineness; but the punched screen appears the better, as it discharges a shade more freely and does not choke quite so easily. It is, however, a little more costly.

Now for cleaning up. Your crushing is through. Slow down the battery. As you hear the stampers thudding perilously close to the naked dies, stop her, otherwise the stamper shoes would be falling on the bare steel of the dies. Those five stampers must be lifted up. To do this, turn the fly-wheel of the engine by hand and place a piece of wood on the guide so that the tappet will catch on it when it comes off the cam. Thus, you hang the whole five stampers up out of the way while you are cleaning up the box the hole.

XXIII

Amalgamation (continued)

Cleaning up: Retorting: Smelting

Cleaning Up.—Clean the plates first: they appear all "ridgy" with amalgam. Where it is hard, slice the ridges off with a thin table-knife. Don't scratch the plates; keep the knife-blade down on the surface without letting the blade dig in. Where the amalgam is soft, scrape it off with a piece of square, hard rubber.

Don't clean the plate right to the bare copper unless you are in desperate need of gold. By leaving a little amalgam on the plate, it will help considerably in saving the gold when you silver up again for the next crushing. With the amalgam you will, of course, get beads of quicksilver that have not collected any gold. After cleaning the plates, sprinkle on a little "silver" and dress them.

Now for your box. Place a board across the tables, put the cleaning-up tub on the board and fill it with water. With a scrubbing-brush wash everything into the tub that has been in contact with amalgam. Then take out the screen and wash it. With a small steel bar dig the dies out and scrub and clean them. Loosen with the bar the residue in the box. You have already made a small hopper or screen, about 12 in. x 12 in. x 4 in. deep with a sheet-iron bottom. With a round punch cut quarter-inch holes in the bottom. Punch with the iron bottom firm on hardwood, so that you will take the piece clean out without burring.

Now place the prospecting dish in the bottom of the tub; place the hopper on top of the dish: take a small shovelful out of the box and put it in the hopper, stir with your hand and shake until all the fines have gone through into the dish. What remains in the hopper, place in a heap. Examine it for coarse pieces of amalgam, then pan your dish of fines back into the tub. The amalgam that you collect place in your grinding bowl (porcelain with a pestle of porcelain). When all the sands are cleaned out of the box, wash

131

it out carefully. Lumps of amalgam may get pounded into queer places—on the stamper-shoes, along the side of the box, up above, anywhere. This final, thorough washing of the box all goes out on to the plates which you have already dressed.

Save your hopperings to put back into the box when setting the dies for the next crushing. Again dress your plates. Turn the water on lightly. "Feed" your fines from the tub on to the lip of the box, distributing evenly, with just enough water to carry the fines over the plates. Finally, wash out your tub over the plates. Turn the water off: get to the plates with your hard rubber: have the bowl handy: lift this new amalgam off with the knife. Now all your amalgam and silver is in the bowl. Run your magnet through it to take out the ground iron. Save all your "magnetings": they contain some values and can be treated later. Save all old worn-out hand rags—in fact, anything that has been in contact with the silver.

So you clean all iron out. Grind it well with the pestle, keeping it covered with water. Spread your flannel over the dish: pour the water from the bowl and wring the flannel into your dish. Now, the amalgam will be in the bottom of your bowl with "silver" on top. Mineral may be floating on top of the "silver": you can "sweep" this mineral off. Put everything you sweep off aside, for future grinding. Now wet a strong piece of calico. Pour your silver and amalgam into the dish: place the calico in the bowl and pour the silver and amalgam back into it. Then, gather up the outside edges of the calico and, starting from the top, "screw" the calico, wringing it tightly. Keep one hand working down towards the quick-silver. Squeeze and work very tightly until the excess of "silver" is squeezed out, while the amalgam is squeezed into a ball. Then open the cloth, wash down beads of "silver" that have gathered on the sides and squeeze very tightly again. The result is a ball of amalgam ready for the retort.

In the silver squeezed through, there will be a little value in gold. You recover that when again utilizing the silver.

Retorting.—This means to separate your gold from the quicksilver. A small iron retort goes with every battery. It is quite simple to use but, like giving a baby a feeding-bottle, you must do the job properly.

To clean the retort. Get a little battery slime, wet it, and rub it round the inside of the retort. This prevents the gold from sticking to the retort. Put your amalgam in one half of the retort and fasten the other half down. Then put the retort on the forge or a **slow** fire, but **build the fire round the sides and top, not under the bottom**. Do not forget this. The heat soon begins to drive the quicksilver away. Liven the fire. The mercury as vapour flows down the retort-tube, the end of which is placed in a vessel with water. Care should be taken to keep the outlet covered with the water. The vapour, on coming into contact with the water in the receptacle condenses again into quicksilver ready for future use. When you see (by the diminution of vapour coming from the retort-tube) that you have driven most of the silver from the gold, liven the fire considerably to drive the last silver away. Then remove the retort and allow it to cool. When you open the retort the gold will be there in a spongy mass.

Smelting. Now you smelt it. Smelting is a simple operation, but if you don't do it properly you are liable to lose the gold.

Get a plumbago crucible and some powdered borax. Put some of the borax in the crucible bottom. Then break up your retorted gold, drop some in the crucible and sprinkle borax over it. Then add more gold and more borax. Use plenty of borax; it makes slag and the gold flows better. When all the gold is in, cover it lightly with borax. Now, with the tongs, place your crucible well and firmly down in the forge fire—a **slow** fire, mind. As the pot warms, the borax begins to crackle and melt. Blow up a steady heat on the forge and keep it steady until the gold melts. Have your mould ready on the fire and it. Put a piece of candle-grease in and be sure that the warmth smears the grease all over the mould. If your mould is not warm the molten gold is liable to "splash." Place your mould in the gold dish, thus catching any "prills" if through carelessness or otherwise you splash in pouring the gold.

When the gold is melted, grasp the crucible with the tongs and pour the gold steadily into the mould, pouring faster towards the end.

Remember, always keep your crucible in a dry place. If it is damp when put in the fire, it cracks and away goes your gold. If you are "breaking in" a new crucible, always warm it in the fire before using. Do that if you like with any crucible—it may be damp and you may not know it.

When the mould is cold, turn it smartly over and out drops your bar of gold.

You may look at it with mixed feelings. You have worked for weeks, have crushed tons of stone, and the result is these few ounces of yellow metal. You feel like a man who has swallowed the sea and not had much of a drink.

However, weigh that gold. Multiply the number of ounces by the value per ounce, divide the result by the number of weeks you have worked for the crushing, and you get what you have made per week. Anyway, you may clean up a few hundred ounces "next crushing." So prepare your battery for the "next."

A nice speed for an ordinary five-head battery, such as this, is about forty-five revolutions per minute, which gives ninety drops of the stampers per minute. The height of the drop all depends on the class of stone you are crushing. For ordinary quartz, a six or seven inch drop is usual. The harder the stone, the higher the drop required; with, of course, consequent harder work on the battery. If your battery has cross-keyed tappets, it is quite easy to alter the drop as you wish. The capacity of this plant is three tons in eight hours. It is driven by a 6 h.p. steam engine, by a belt from a pulley on the engine to the pulley on the counter-shaft.

I would advise you, however, to drive your battery by a crude oil engine. Although one man works the above plant, it really is the job of three: one to cut and draw wood, another to look after the boiler and fire her, and a man to watch the battery and feed it. Besides, a man has to have an engine-driver's certificate under the Mining Act.

Crude oil is a one-man job, and the cost of oil would be under £2 for forty-eight hours' run. About an eight-horse brakepower would drive this battery and the pump.

So there is a description of a working battery, kept working by one man, from the mining of the ore to the smelting of the gold. You and your mates should be as good men as he. But I doubt if you could come up to my old mate Lige.

XXIV

Battery Work:

Complex Ores Cleaning "Silver"

Batteries are all on the same principle. There are never more than five stampers in one box. With heavier stampers more stone is put through, but the battery is more expensive. The stamps generally weigh from 1000 lb. to 1400 lb. A ten-head battery is just as easy to drive as a five-head. Timber frames are generally used, timber being less costly and easier to shift. Extra large batteries have iron frames; although it has been found that wood absorbs the heavy vibration better than iron. In some batteries, the mortar (or stamper) box (or iron) is sometimes fitted with a copper amalgamating plate in a back "pocket," sometimes on the sides too. Also, a chuck block is used for regulating the discharge above the dies instead of packing up the dies with quartz. Some mortar boxes have an amalgamating plate at back and front. But these are minor details.

The quantity of ore you can put through depends on the number of stamps, the height of drop and number of drops per minute, the quality of stone to be crushed, the kind of screens used, the efficiency of discharge, and the quantity of water used. The weight of stamp, as time goes on, is slightly variable, due to the wearing down of die and shoe. You can neutralize this by increasing the height of drop. Your ore may be brittle, soft, hard, clogging, flinty, or spongy. It may go easily through the screen or it may have tendency to clog. These little details and their remedies you learn by experience.

When feeding the battery, just keep adding the amount of stone that the stampers can nicely dispose of. If you add too much feed to the mortar box the stamps sound dull, not being able to fall heavily on the dies. If you put in too little the stamp-shoes soon clang on the bare dies. When that happens, feed in more stone quickly. A good plan is to put a chalk mark round the stamp-stems just above the guides. That lets you see at a glance how much stone is on the dies.

You will hardly need a rock-breaker. Truck your stone into the feeding-chute just as you take it from the mine. Later, when feeding the battery, give any oversize stone a clout with a hammer; you will have plenty of time. The stampers won't mind if you feed in stone as big as your fist.

Complex Ores.—The majority of auriferous ores contain "free" gold. Hence you will generally have no trouble in crushing, separating, and saving your gold. However, some ores are complex, that is, gold is present in the stone in chemical combination with other minerals—for example: iron pyrites, arsenical pyrites, antimony, bismuth, copper. And there may be present in yet other ores, zinc, lead, sulphides, etc.

These complex ores are the very devil. They require special treatment. This book cannot go into details.

If you find a decent proposition with complex ore your best plan will be to sell it to a company who can afford to erect a special plant for treatment. Or you can erect an ordinary battery with a few special treatment tables and accessories for saving the concentrates. By that means you save in the box and on the plates whatever free gold is liberated from the stone. The concentrates you send away to a treatment plant: the tailings you yourself put through cyanide vats.

You must learn a little about cyanidation. If your ore is too complex to treat efficiently through the battery, it is also complex for cyanide; and necessitates a knowledge of the cyanidation of complex ores.

When sulphides are present to excess in stone, a dark-coloured scum soon starts to form on the plates, generally "sickening" the amalgam which "scours" off. Additional quicksilver every hour raises the percentage of extraction. Arsenic is the very devil when present in excess in stone.

Here is a tip, on the treatment of complex ore, from the latest developments in South Africa, where the science of battery work is probably the most developed in the world. Use corduroy cloth on your concentrating tables. In latest South African practice it is actually claimed that an ordinary battery, with properly arranged corduroy tables, has been proved to treat complex ores without any special appliances.

So there is a wonderfully cheap process that many an abandoned "complex ore" mine in Australia might take advantage of.

Always keep your plates bright and clean. If a plate shows verdigris, it means the copper in or under the amalgam is oxidized by air and water. Then again, copper may have been in the ore, or you may have used chemicals in dressing the plate. Perhaps the cause is too thin a coating of amalgam on the plate.

Many such stains are easily soluble by your cyanide solution. Simply wash them with that; but wash off the solution afterwards, as cyanide has a solvent power on gold too. The softer you can keep your amalgam, the better "reception" it has for gold. Leave at least a little amalgam on the plates when you clean up. It takes the quicksilver easier and helps with the saving of gold in the next crushing. Too much "silver," however, is sometimes liable to "soften" the amalgam which, then, is liable to form into sharp ridges and points that might break off and become lost in the tailings.

Some men "electroplate" their plates with quicksilver. This electroplating is a good idea for catching very fine gold from "pulp" ores.

There are many tricks in amalgamation. Learn all you can. I saw a good dodge once which you may apply. An old digger had cut grooves to act as ripples on his tables above and below his plates. These grooved ripples caught numerous beads of "silver" which had not joined with the amalgam on the plates. They caught beads of amalgam too, and also grains of freed gold. He cleaned out his wells, dished the concentrates in these wells, and got numerous beads of "silver," amalgam, and free gold. He wished to amalgamate this little haul; that is, to make the "silver" take up itself, and the gold in one lump. He got a clean enamel bucket and with clean hands poured a little kerosene in it. Then, not allowing his hands or grease to touch the washing, he plunged them into the bucket.

Amalgamation was practically instantaneous.

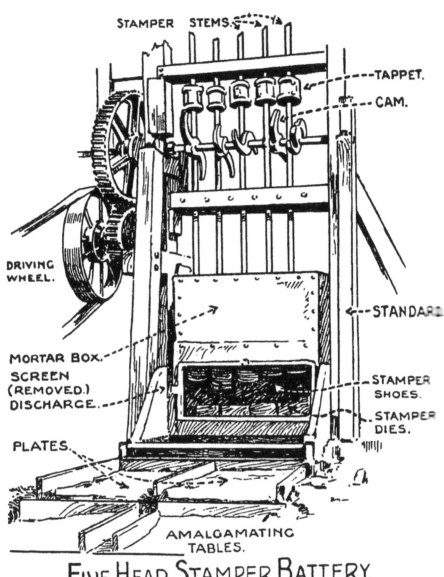

STAMPER STEMS.

TAPPET.

CAM.

DRIVING WHEEL.

STANDARD

MORTAR BOX.

SCREEN (REMOVED.)

DISCHARGE.

STAMPER SHOES.

STAMPER DIES.

PLATES.

AMALGAMATING TABLES.

FIVE HEAD STAMPER BATTERY.

There are numerous such "tricks."

You will have a lot to do with quicksilver. It is expensive, but you can use it over and over your "silver" before using, it won't form good amalgam; it won't save all the gold. There are quite a number of things it won't do that it ought to do. It all depends on the amount of grease, dirt, and other impurities you have left in it.

A good way to clean quicksilver is to wash it in a weak solution of nitric acid.

Silver when used and retorted again for use, may contain copper, arsenic, lead, etc., if your stone has carried a small percentage of these ores.

I have seen quicksilver plunged into kerosene, then stirred briskly with a wooden paddle. The kerosene turns black; it absorbs the lead and perhaps other impurities, leaving the silver bright and clean.

Another dodge, when your quicksilver "sickens" owing to impurities such as arsenic and antimony being absorbed, is to put it in a clean enamel bucket and stir thoroughly with a wooden ladle.

A scummy dross comes to the surface. Wipe that off with a sponge, and repeat the stirring and sponging until the surface becomes bright and the silver runs freely. This should clean it of all but those minerals actually dissolved in it. A sprinkling of nitrate of soda will then often clear it up. Sodium peroxide is better still.

Some men never use clay to line their retort or tighten the cover. They prefer chalk or whiting. The clay often discolours the gold. Men say the price then is not so good. That is a matter of opinion. Clay, however, under the heat, is liable to crack and, if your retort is not tight, a pin-head or two of gold may "spit" away.

XXV

Cyanide Poisoning and cure:

Cleaning up Old Battery Sites

Cyanide poisoning and cure.—When you are handling cyanide, if you have any cuts or sores, you may be susceptible to "cyanide sores." Some men are not. Again, suppose you swallow just a drop of cyanide, well, get rid of it quickly if you don't want to be a premature angel. Here's a cure that an old cyanide man gave me. I can't guarantee it, for I've never seen it tried, but here it is: Drink ferrous sulphate followed by sodium bi-carbonate. A purgative should then be taken and the patient forced to walk about to prevent him sleeping. Tickle his throat with finger or feather to cause vomiting—a tumblerfull of warm water and mustard is a good help. Be quick.

Cleaning up old battery sites.—Here are a few wrinkles. Perhaps you are carrying the swag, are broke, and nobody loves you. Off the road you see an old battery site. Nothing there now but a rusted boiler and the charred stumps of the shed, all overgrown by grass and looking as forlorn as you feel. Not at all. That ruin may be worth £100 to you.

In the course of years, gold is inevitably lost in battery work. The greater the quantity and the richer the stone put through the more gold is lost. But, if someone has been before you that is your stiff luck. I know battery sites that have been cleaned up five times by five different men—and each got gold. Each knew a little more than the preceding one: that was why.

First, scratch round for the forge site. Most likely the gold was retorted and smelted here. Crucibles have burst probably j moulds have splashed. Carelessness and inexperience in other ways have split molten gold and mislaid amalgam; amalgam beads have "squirted," splashed, leaked, or run away. If there is any stone or brick-work of the forge left, pull it apart. Examine every brick or stone. Is spilt slag adhering to it? Perhaps you see "prills" of gold adhering in the slag; dirty leaden pellets of amalgam wedged in between the stone. Scrape, chisel, or tomahawk off all slag. Save it. Dig six inches deep under and all round where the forge was. Bag that earth and hump it to the creek. Dish it somehow. You will get a mixture: prills of gold, lead, amalgam, "silver," nails, copper rivets, bits of steel, pickheads, centipedes, files, worms, boot-heels, rusty meat-tin lids, grubs and other curios. Sort it all out, saving all prills, scraps of slag, amalgam "stirrer" wires—everything you think may have come in contact with smelted gold. Remember the amalgam pieces will look like dirty bits of lead buried for years. Test them: if they are lead they will mark paper. If your luck is in, you may find some fine big pieces of amalgam and numerous pellets of gold, dirty-looking from exposure to atmospheric conditions. Scratch every likely thing and see if the yellow glistens underneath. Next, find the ash-heap. Pull the grass off it: hump the whole lot to the creek and put it through: dig a little race and chuck it in if it is a big heap. You will get another motley collection out of the ash-heap. Separate and classify it—and don't get a rusted or copper nail in your finger-tip. Then, find where they have tipped the old crucibles. Here may be a fruitful source of gold. In those days plumbago crucibles were seldom used. Examine the slag adhering to all crucibles j there may be prills of gold in it. Cracked crucibles may have quite a lot of gold in the cracks. All such payable fragments, slag, etc., put aside to dolly and wash later.

Next, find where the tables were. Dig up under and round for a depth of six inches. Put the dirt through. If you are being paid for your work it may well pay you to dig up all round the battery.

Examine any old stamper-heads, shoes, or dies for amalgam. Examine carefully the old mortar box; dig under it. Scrape, root, and scratch about everywhere. Look for iron "stirrers" which may have been used for stirring slag or gold. If the remains of the old plates are about, heat and sweat them, scrape off all traces of amalgam. Pour boiling water over the plate, sprinkle it with clean quicksilver and scour it well, using a piece of flat hardwood while continually using boiling water.

Wash the tailings off. If you have a piece of hard cyanide, rub and scrape the plate. Wash with boiling water, then scrape with hard rubber.

Finally, smelt the fruits of your labour. If you can't do it there (you ought to be able to, you should be able to do just about anything in gold mining now) hurry your spoil to the nearest bank, where they will send it away for smelting, or advise you where to send it.

I have cleaned up to £70 worth of gold on abandoned battery sites more than once. And I know of other men who have cleaned up over £200 worth. Such a source of revenue is not universally known. You know it now. Providing the site has not previously been cleaned up, there is gold there for you if much stone has been put through in the years gone by.

If you are working a tin-lode, crushing the stone is quite similar. But you save your tin in boxes or tables, and do not use copper plates or amalgam.

XXVI

Opal-Mining—Black Opals

Sinking: Driving: Gouging:Snipping

Now for our Australian opal, the best in the world. That is no boast: our gems hold the world's markets. In the black opal, Australia has a unique gem. The only known black-opal field in the world is here. The black opals from Lightning Ridge are of such ravishing beauty that they beggar description.

Opals occur in the desert sandstones. A huge belt of this country runs nearly across Australia, from Queensland and New South Wales into Centralia, embracing South Australia with its Stuart Range fields, and in places penetrating Western Australia. New South Wales and Queensland have the greatest opal-fields yet found. The Coober Pedy country in South Australia has produced a rich field, and other fields are almost sure to be found in the Stuart Range in that State. Opals have also been found in Western Australia and the Northern Territory.

There are two varieties of opals: "light" and "black." The chief market for these gems is Hatton Gardens, London. Other markets are New York, Paris, Berlin, Vienna, and among the rich maharajahs of India. A unique gem will sometimes bring thousands of pounds.

Black opals.—It is remarkable that we do not get far higher prices for our black opals. There is a world market for them, and there is only one field producing them in all the world. When that field becomes exhausted what will the price of black opals be then?

Opals cannot be manufactured synthetically! This is not the only instance where we wideawake (?) Australians are letting the fruits of a world monopoly slip through our fingers. **We** should fix the price of the black opal—**not** the buyers.

In sandstone country, watch the ground. Should you see a small black or dirty-grey stone that hardly looks like a stone, strike it. If it cracks or breaks like coarse glass, it is probably "potch," that is, worthless opal. Examine it for "colour." There may be a faint flash of red, green, or orange in it that the weather has not quite destroyed.

The potch sometimes "comes out" like that on the sides of ridges. Under the sandstone cap may be a layer of "opal dirt"—a level. Where this level pokes out from the ridge, weather and rain have washed out any opal the jutting portion may have contained and deposited it a little further down the hill, among the grass where you "speck" it. Down the ridge yet another level, camouflaged by loam and grass and perhaps ironstone pebbles, may jut out. That is how White Cliffs was found, a field that supported three thousand people for many years. A kangaroo shooter there "specked" potch.

Be keen-eyed. Opal dirt does not resemble wash dirt. There are no stones in it, no gravel or sand or loam. Working in opal dirt is like tunnelling into a wall of soft rock (occasionally it is very hard), consequently you have no wash to guide you. Also, invariably you locate opal up under the roof; not on a hard bottom as with gold or tin. You go right through bottom to get your opal, and that bottom becomes your roof. In prospecting, you don't go dishing creeks and gullies. Opal is a comparatively light stone, it would rarely be found in a gully. Further, all opal country found so far is "dry."

Hence, all you have to guide you is your luck. All opal-fields have been found by the specking of potch and colour.

Sinking.—So, you sink "on the blind." You may go four feet, or forty. You may sink until your heart or windlass fails. If you do not strike opal dirt, sink again, say a quarter of a mile farther on. Once you locate opal dirt, sooner or later a lucky shaft may strike opal. On a known held, you have the old workings as a guide to locality and depth. In each known opal district, there is an area of from thirty to one hundred miles of proved opal country which has not yet known a pick!

Opal occurs not only as a patch in a claim, but as big patches in a field. A field may be, say, ten miles in length. But there may be only areas of a quarter-mile in length (perhaps only a couple of hundred yards) along that ten-mile strip, which carry the precious opal. Long and dashed wide blanks in between keep you guessing. You have to find such a patch to locate a field.

Then the rush comes and each "gouger" must locate a patch within his claim even though that claim be pegged in the centre of an already proved field. Opal gouging is "patchy."

Then again, each "run" of opal is generally very narrow. A hundred to three hundred yards in width of actual opal-bearing ground is considered good. As you work your claim, and locate opal, the run within your ground may be only a few yards in length and a few feet in width. However, there may be a number of such runs within your claim. A number of such claims adjacent to each other make up a field. If it is a large field, then the area described may be alluded to in a broad sense as a "patch." The next patch may be three, five, miles away, the spreading out, as patch after patch is discovered, being the field."

You start your shaft, say, in black-opal country. The shallower country from the grass roots down has already been taken up. You expect to "bottom" at fourteen feet. Bottom in this instance, means breaking through the last of the sandstone into the opal dirt. Make your shaft approximately five feet long by two feet six inches wide, make it just comfortable to work in. The larger you make it the more rock you must pick and shovel out. Make the corners "round" if you can, not "square." An experienced man can "throw out" to a depth of ten feet. However, there is no need to break yourself. Log up and put the windlass on at eight or nine feet.

When about two feet from the bottom, the sandstone grows harder, ending in the steel-like band just as you break through. Thousands of pounds' worth of valuable opals have been won in this thin, flinty hard band. Far more have been got **under** the band, which is the "roof." Many claims, however, have no steel band, you just break through the sandstone on to the opal dirt. Opal is generally found (if at all) a foot or more down in the opal dirt. I have worked opal at a depth of twelve feet in the opal dirt. But such a claim is unusual. As you "bottom," you experience a wonderful feeling, no matter how many duffers you have previously sunk. This time you may open up a "jeweller's shop." It is thirty to one that you won't. But no matter: "Live in hope if you die in despair" is the opal gouger's motto.

Use the pick carefully on breaking through, for if your luck is in you may break a £50 stone. Quite possibly you will "hear" the opal before you see it. If you hear glass gritting or breaking you have put your pick into potch or a "stone." Your heart leaps into your mouth. You drop to your knees, scratch in the opal dirt and nearly howl at the sight of fragments of gold and orange. You bawl to your mate that you've "broke a lovely gem." He sends down a sheath-knife, a "spider," or a gouging pick. Carefully you gouge the stone out, examine it, then yell in delight that you've "only chipped it."

Perhaps you bottom on potch and colour, but no precious opal. Well, sink on cheerfully. There is a good chance of that "colour" leading you, when you begin to drive, to a patch or "pocket" of opal.

Potch and colour is opal, but not "precious." It is "young opal" (so called) and has little or no value, but it is the only indication of the, perhaps, close proximity of precious opal that the gouger has.

Driving.—Now, if you bottom a duffer it means you have got nothing, no potch or colour even. Many men abandon such a shaft to sink another and another. This is not a wise plan. Sink down through your opal dirt to a depth of six feet; then "drive" from either end or side of the shaft. In starting the "drive" chamber out; that is, cut out a small chamber. This gives you room to throw your mullock as you drive on, and allows uncramped room to shovel your mullock into the buckets. Now start your drive proper. You are driving "on the blind" and don't want to dig, shovel, and haul one bucket of unnecessary mullock. According to the size of man you are and your adaptability for working in a small place, so you make your drive; height, say, four feet; width, three feet. You sit back on your heels and drive ahead, using a short-handled three-pound driving-pick. You will soon get used to the space. The dirt is soft, the work pleasant. Using the little shovel, you shovel over your shoulder back into the drive behind you. There is a knack in the sway of your body and the "throw" of the shovel as the dirt goes over your shoulder. You will soon get into it. What doesn't go over will get into your ear.

Thump the spider in the wall beside you and drive on, keeping the sandstone as your roof. (The spider is the twisted piece of fencing-wire, or the bought steel spike, which holds your candle.) From the roof to a foot down, is the place where opal will almost certainly occur if you are going to "strike it," so watch this "face" most closely and place the candle to light it up when you are picking just there.

Opal, potch and colour will most likely "come in" directly under the roof, or a few inches down; possibly in a reddish, gritty seam. Chip expectantly if such a seam comes in. Should you hit a stone, or potch and colour you will hear the "crack." Hold the candle against the face and look for colour. If you see a flash of orange, green or red in the potch, then you have hit a stone. Gouge it out with the point of the spider, with a knife, or the chisel-end of the pick. Go as circumspectly as if you were tickling your ladylove's ear. There may be a £40 stone there, and you don't want to break your heart.

Being on a black-opal field, you may have struck a "pocket" of "nobbys," or a patch. (A pocket is a cluster of stones: there may be twenty, there may be two hundred.) When the pocket is exhausted drive on looking for another. A patch means, generally, hundreds of stones. You may be weeks, months, "on opal."

If you strike potch, follow it. If potch and colour, follow them carefully until they lead you to opal or they "cut out." Be very careful when on potch and colour—at any moment they may "make" into a "stone."

Gouging.—The rule followed when on colour or opal is to "gouge" the dirt to a depth down from the roof of eighteen inches. This gouging is a careful chip, chip, chipping with the light gouging pick; then "chip" the scraping of the chisel-edge gliding on a stone without shattering it and the grating "feel" of the pick against the stone (even though there be no sound) betray it.

As you thus gouge in under the roof, you form a ledge. The dirt from the seam or seams falls on this ledge. Examine it carefully (if on opal) before brushing it to the floor. Occasionally you will find a stone on that ledge, which you have picked out unawares from the face.

When you have gouged in as far as possible for comfort, belt into the "toe" of the face. This toe is the opal dirt below the ledge. Pick it away lustily though cautiously. When you have "squared" the face, carefully gouge under the roof again.

These opals are called stones or nobbies, because they look such; little nobbies of opal camouflaged with opal dirt. Often they are the shape of a walnut. Often larger and much flatter. They may cluster together like a bunch of big but hidden plums, or they may be spread fairly evenly along the red, gritty seam. They may be, and often are, plastered up against the sandstone roof like oysters on a rock. Potch may be black, grey, white, milky, green, blue, glassy, etc . And so may opal. Abundance of light opal is also found amongst the black.

Opal-gouging is clean and comfortable work; cool in summer, warm in winter, and no working in water and timbering. The only timber used is that for logging up the "collar" of the shaft on which to place the windlass. As the dump grows higher, you shift the windlass, put on a few more logs, replace the windlass, and away you go again. An odd "torn" is occasionally put in underground when you strike an exceptionally large patch of opal and have to chamber out a huge space in the opal dirt. A torn is a prop, you jam one end under the roof with the other end resting on the floor. Sandstone generally makes an ideal roof. Most men when chambering, leave pillars of opal dirt as supports, then come back later and gouge out these pillars: others do it when the claims are abandoned. Many thousands of pounds worth of opals have been gouged from such pillars. I, myself, in a month gouged £700 worth from one abandoned pillar.

If you get tired of driving on the blind, "come up" and sink another shaft wherever fancy prompts. Some men cannot drive unless they are on opal. I think it is a matter of psychology. These men will sink day after day, belting like slaves down into the sandstone perhaps for a depth of ninety feet, only to strike a duffer and immediately start another one. They slave in the hope of striking opal directly below. I look at opal- mining in this way: Perhaps it takes you a month to sink a shaft for only one day's work in opal dirt. If that month had been spent in driving the last shaft you sank, you would have driven approximately one hundred and twenty feet in opal dirt, in any foot of which you may have struck opal. However, every man to his own psychology.

Snipping.—As you gouge out the nobby from the "face," examine it. It is coated with dirt, but the potch generally is visible here and there. Turn it round slowly in your fingers, and watch closely for a flash of colour. Ah! there it is! Hold it to the candle. See if the colour runs round the stone in a "band;" that is, if a strip, or thread or bar of colour runs right through the stone. You can only guess from that dull wisp of colour at the edges. Carefully chip the edge here and there with a sharp snips. (Price, generally one shilling on the field.) This just cuts a tiny chip out of the potch edge and the colour blazes out. You smile like a man who has won the Lottery, for that blaze of red, gold, and orange on inky black potch reveals a good stone, perhaps a gem. Lingeringly you put it in the bag with the others; you will examine it in the light of day lest you snip too deeply and damage the stone.

It is a glorious feeling being "on opal." It gives a man a thrill like nothing else on earth; especially if your credit is exhausted at the store.

Now, when you strike a patch, don't go mad: don't rush up the shaft and tell the world about it. It is hard to refrain I know; but keep your luck to yourself for a while. Otherwise, you may go down your shaft next morning and find it "ratted."

Ratters are men, a gang as a rule, who work your opal out for you while you sleep. My mate went "mad" when we struck our first pocket of opal. Next morning we went down the shaft to find the drive mullocked up, the "face" gouged out, chips of beautiful opal lying everywhere, showing with what ruthless haste the ratters had worked. We lost hundreds of pounds that night.

XXVII

Opal-Mining—Light Opals
Facing: Classing: Selling

Having found your opals, you next class, "face," value, and sell them. There are two ways of selling opals, "in the rough," and "faced." In the rough means the unfaced stones, with a snip taken here and there round the edges.

Now, be canny in snipping. You want to gain an approximate value and to form your opinion as to whether the stone will "cut" (face). Further, if selling in the rough, you want to show the stone to the best advantage and not emphasize its faults. If you snip it too much and reveal "sand holes," "bad back" (not much potch that the jeweller could use as a mounting), dull, smoky, or irregular colours, then each misjudged snip lowers the value of your stone. Remember, the buyer will prove a very keen, very experienced man. So try and snip each stone so as to emphasize the good colour only.

A stone in the rough may appear worth £5. When faced, it may prove to be worth £20, or it may not be worth five bob. Some opals are sand-pitted, others are milky, cloudy, smoky, broken barred, etc. Judge by the "bar" and the brilliance of the colour. Many opals have a bar of colour running through them. If this bar shows well defined under the snips, and the colour is brilliant, then most likely the stone will "face out."

You may get £300 for a parcel in the rough. Faced out that parcel might be worth £700—quite likely considerably more. On the other hand, if you face it and it doesn't "turn out" you may not realise £50 for it. In more ways than one, opal gouging is a fascinating gamble. Most men sell their opals faced, for the majority of stones "turn out."

There are cutters on most opal-fields, generally charging 6d. per stone. This is quite inexpensive. But it can be expensive if in your inexperience you hand in a parcel of potch and colour which face out all "sixpenny duds."

On any well-established field the majority of men possess their own "wheel," a tool similar to a dentist's lathe and costing about £3. It is a pedal-worked lathe, with coarse and fine carborundum wheels and coarse, medium and fine carborundum paper. A felt wheel and a tin of jeweller's rouge completes the equipment.

The advantage in cutting your own opals, apart from saving money, is the interest and delight the work gives you. There is the further advantage of being able to keep quiet about your find as long as you like.

Facing.—Now you have your parcel snipped, ready for the wheel. (Never snip a stone unless that is necessary.) Above your wheel hangs a piece of fencing-wire with a treacle-tin attached. Punch a hole in the bottom of the tin and fill it with water. The "drip," "drip," of the water on the wheel stops the dust from being inhaled by you.

Now pick up your first stone. (Always try your hand on potch and colour until you get into the way of it.) Before you put that stone on the wheel be certain that you will face the "face" and not the "back" of the stone. The colouring on the bar, and experience will teach you. Of course, if you are one of those new chums who go to an opal-field and "bottom on it" first go, give your opals to a professional cutter. Then, stand by to see them faced and to quickly learn. If you try to face a parcel without first having seen it done and picking up a little experience, you will almost certainly destroy many valuable stones.

To return to your wheel. Press your foot on the pedal and the wheel goes round. Hold the stone to the wheel and grind off the outer covering of dirt and potch. Keep dipping the stone in a tobacco-tin of water beside you. Each dip shows up the potch, the bar, the colour. As you grind away the potch, so the clearer and clearer you see the colour, the bar forming. Do not remove all the potch from the top of the bar, leave just a film of potch over it. Then unscrew the coarse wheel and screw on the medium or fine. (Stones with but little potch only require medium and fine.) Now grind away carefully the last of the potch.

Some bar stones have the colour "thick;" others are thin as paper. A beautiful stone may possess only a film of colour. One turn of the wheel too many may blur or destroy its "pattern," may take the brightness "out of the colour," and will certainly take five guineas from its value.

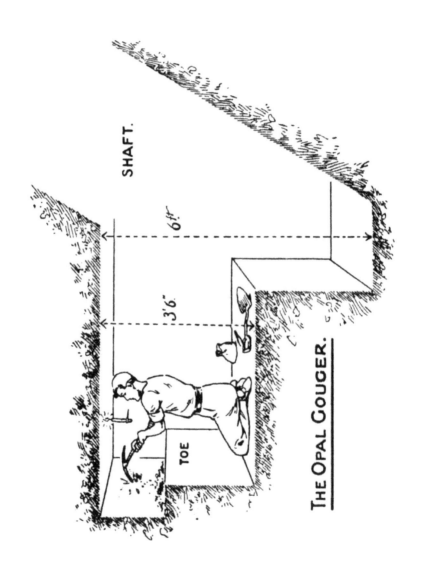

Dip the stone repeatedly in the water. As you grind deeper into the potch, so the colours "come up." You need to take off just sufficient potch to leave the brightest colour showing. Don't grind right down into the colour unless it is dull with brighter showing underneath. So, take off your wheel, and put on a cardboard wheel covered with a disk of coarse carborundum or emery paper clipped out with scissors. Peddle again and grind down into the colour, cutting dull colour away and "bringing out" brilliance. Be very careful. When you are almost on to the most brilliant colour, take off the coarse emery and put on medium. Then replace that with fine. This fine emery removes all the scratches made by the coarse emery. Next put on the felt wheel, wet it and with a wet shaving brush put jeweller's rouge on the wheel. Finally polish the stone and polish it well. Some men "dry polish."

In cutting (facing) a stone the object is to bring out the most brilliant colours, and pattern. Some stones have no "pattern." You know what that is: you see it in the carpet every day. A pattern stone, if the colours are bright, is the most valuable, and of all patterns the Harlequin is, perhaps, the most prized.

The squares, oblongs, and other markings in any pattern stone generally flash in different colours. There are flame stones, liquid, opal, fire, orange green, wave, pin-fire, diamond, and other names. A wave stone is one in which as you move it a wave of colour comes floating over the stone: a fire-stone is one in which red predominates, and so on. "Fire," or "flame," in a stone is the most valuable colour as "harlequin" is the most prized pattern.

If you find a "sandspit" in the centre of your lovely stone, well, that is your bad luck. Don't grind and grind, hoping to grind it out. Examine the stone and see how deep the colour goes. If the sand goes deeper, you must leave the sand. Face your stone to the best advantage. The buyer will cut the stone in half, or the jeweller will put a diamond where the sand was.

Similarly, if a "cloud" has formed over the most beautiful colour spot on your stone. If that cloud goes right through the colour you can't remove it. A cloud is a film. "Smoky" means much the same.

Experience will soon teach you many of the numerous points in facing opal. It is a fascinating game. If you get a "double-bar" stone or any good stone in which the colour film is particularly thin, give it to the professional cutter.

Classing and Selling.—Having faced your parcel, you now class it. Experienced diggers find it a pleasure to do this for you. Sometimes a field has classers and valuers, who do the work at a small charge. Generally, men don't face their opals until they have cut the potch out. Then it sometimes pays to advertise. Buyers get to hear that So-and-so has a good parcel. If several buyers happen to visit the field together you can enjoy the fruits of competition.

In classing, a parcel may be separated into gem stones, first, seconds, and so on down to potch and colour. Or, the gouger may prefer his opals "all blacks," "near blacks," "light," etc., or he may divide the stones into parcels with one "gem" in each. The gems help to sell the parcels. Some men will refuse to sell the parcel "split up." "Take all or none." Buyers often have a ready market for some classes of opals and an uncertain market for others. Hence, any buyer will give a few pounds more for the class he wants.

But every gouger hates the "eyes" being picked out of his parcel, as when a buyer picks out the gems and offers a price for those alone. Gem and first quality stones are always easy to sell. A man may have to keep inferior stones for months. A large opal-field may have a number of resident buyers. Others visit periodically from the cities; while continental buyers come now and again. The gouger invariably puts a price on his parcel above what he expects. He seldom gets what he first asks.

Some classes of opal, particularly those "lights" that come from such a field as White Cliffs and several of the Queensland opal districts, sell opals by weight, gem stuff so much per carat, others, as a rule, so much per ounce. On "the Cliffs" and other fields, the opal generally occurs in seams, such a seam being much more continuous than "nobbys."

There is generally a second, third, and fourth level on an opal-field. The biggest fields in Australia have been declared "worked out" until some digger sank down through the opal dirt, then through the succeeding sandstone, to find a second layer of opal dirt twenty or thirty feet below. Numerous second levels have proved richer than the first, and have given a second and third lease of life to the field.

In the known opal-bearing districts of Australia there are some hundreds of miles of country which have never known a pick. Apart from known districts, there are certainly big fields yet to be discovered.

"Noodling" is a popular opal-fields pastime. You sit on a dump and scratch it down, searching for stones that have been missed. Thousands of pounds' worth have been recovered by noodlers. On a "nobby" field, noodling is a great standby for the man who is broke. But it is bad for the field, for if the shaft happens to be deserted the noodlers scratch the dump down into the shaft, and perhaps it will never be worked again. Big values in opal have been won by men working abandoned shafts.

Queensland has a number of rich districts. Opalton, Parvo, Windsor, Koroit, Duck Creek, Emu Creek, Springsure, Kyabra, and other districts carry beautiful opals. A rich find has recently been made at Quilpie.

In most Queensland fields, the values occur as "boulder opal." After sinking through the sandstone, an "ironstone band," perhaps a foot in thickness is encountered. The opal runs through this hard band in thin veins. Instead of a solid band, it may be a band of tiny ironstone boulders, sized from a walnut to a clenched fist. Inside an occasional boulder is a "kernel" of opal, hence "kernel opal." The "Yowah nuts," in the Eulo district, are famous. These "nuts" are ironstone packed like pebbles and the kernels have produced gems fit for a queen's purse. "Matrix opal" is opal in many veins running through "the band."

You must be very careful with the "boulders." When you have a large heap on top, sharpen your sharpest tomahawk and gently chip each boulder and expose the opal, if any. It is an awfully wasteful method. Many beautiful opals are smashed. It is a wonder some thoughtful digger has not evolved a quicker and better method.

In other northern fields, the opal occurs as seams in sandstone boulders encased in a soft shell of coarse sandstone. Yet, again, it is found as "pipe" opal, a pipe of the coloured beauty running through a coarse pipe of sandstone which may be as thick as a man's wrist, perhaps as thick as his body. The opal sometimes occurs in vesicular basalt, and may be present thus in other States.

Many gougers become fascinated by the "Opal Game." They prove to be keen valuers and soon begin to buy and sell among themselves. An odd one among them blossoms forth into a world's buyer.

South Australia carries a long opal-belt in the Stuart Range. In the "gibber" country opal has been proved over an extent of forty miles long by two wide; but there are large areas quite unprospected. The precious opal on

Coober Pedy occurs mostly as bands formed in potch, the bands varying in thickness. The patches are in irregular veins. Some beautiful parcels have been won. Opalized shells and bones of small animals have been mined. Coober Pedy is the blackfellows' name for "White man in a hole." The diggers live in dugouts there. A quick and easy system of prospecting in this country is by hand-auger. The auger is fitted to pipes and hand bored down into the opal dirt. If an opal-seam is bored through, chips show up in the sludge.

Tools for opal-gouging are simple. Windlass and buckets (bullock hide in preference to oil-drums) sinking and driving picks, shorthandled sinking and driving shovels, and a five-shilling bellows for the forge. You will soon buy your own cutting machine when you "strike opal."

For sinking, a couple of four- or five-pound-weight universal picks. Sharpen the picks "diamond" point. For driving, half a dozen two- and three-pound "universals," using a cut down universal handle. Sharpen one end of each driving pick, "diamond" point, the other "chisel." An occasional shaft may go through "shincracker," very hard stone, and may require hammer, drills and gelignite. But the vast majority of opal-country is soft sinking.

XXVIII

You have a Great Chance

Some of you may set out in a rather dubious spirit. Some may say: "Oh well, there's no work in the city, we may as well go and look for gold." Others say: "We wouldn't know how to work gold, even if we found it." Well, in this book, you have the results of a lifetime of experience; an experience that emphasizes the tremendous advantages of modern hydraulics. Never mind how Grandad pottered about with his little tin dish and spade: he did wonderful work; he produced tens of millions of sovereigns; but numbers of you must go over his worked ground; so leave him to his cradle if you can work ground with hydraulic. Remember, men go prospecting in aeroplanes these days—ordinary diggers too, like you are going to be.

After reading this book you will know a great deal. There may be a page or two, here and there, not quite clear. But believe me, immediately you get to work every hint in this book will "come to you" clear as daylight. You will have an immense advantage. You are going out with modern mining knowledge; with the ability in your head to put that knowledge into practice. How immeasurably better off you are than if you went out armed only with a pick and shovel!

Have confidence from the start; it is a wonderful help. When you go on the roads, laugh at your past misgivings. Think of the old-timers who went out in the roaring days, often into country white men had never trod, dependent entirely on their own resources. It is hard for you to visualize what those men faced. Once they passed the last town there was nothing but the "unknown, with all its dangers before them. They battled straight out and pulled through against hardships which very few of you will have to face.

They found gold too. And they saved Australia from a great Depression, and caused the rushes which populated the country.

The old-timers as they spread out and out found field after field and cleaned up the gold (the easy gold) in the older States at least. But much gold has been left, I am convinced. Even in the oldest State there are large areas of auriferous country worth while trying, especially in out of the way regions. And for minerals other than gold.

In three of the States there has been comparatively little prospecting for the last twenty years. The growing cities have called too lustily to youth; and where there is no prospecting being done there is naturally no gold being produced.

No doubt some of you will want to push out into quite new country. Go by all means. You will have an experience that will teach you things about this vast continent of which you never dreamed. But go with at least one experienced bushman in the party. There is wild country yet in Australia; quite a lot of it. There are even areas upon which white men have seldom set foot.

Mind, you must go decently equipped. In northern Australia, in the Nor'-west, and in Centralia, men go out with twelve months' supplies on their pack-horses or camels. Such a start is rather costly. If you haven't the money, and yet you feel inclined for such a venture; then start your experiences much nearer civilization. Learn on safer fields all you can; and by the time you have won enough gold or tin to finance your venture, you will be much better equipped to win through on distant fields.

While you are gaining your experience, remember there are new fields comparatively close at hand yet to be found. A new lease of life awaits some worked fields, particularly alluvial goldfields to which the new prospectors can bring water. I have too often seen what even hand sluicing will produce from old worked ground, not to know what I am talking about in this respect.

In the older States, what the diggers may have missed will very likely prove to be ancient river-beds under the basalt, or almost any rock. Quite recently, in Australia's most northern and isolated goldfield, Batavia River, the diggers have sunk through sandstone and bottomed on payable wash underneath. So far as my knowledge goes, rarely indeed has gold been found in connection with sandstone. Perhaps that is because we have not looked for it. On Batavia River, for twenty years, that tiny band of isolated diggers had been finding some of the best priced gold in Australia in continuous tiny fields near the river, before at last locating gold under the sandstone.

Similarly, in every State many people may be walking over a rich field, hidden under its layer of rock. They did that again at Batavia, only this time the gold was right on the surface. The food supply pack-track for years crossed a gully, *en route* to one of the little fields, and the hoofs of the horses wore a track along which the rain-water ran. It remained for the aboriginal prospector Pluto, to discover Plutoville by seeing a nugget glistening where that track crossed the gully.

By the way, Bill Baird, the prospector of the Batavia, was speared by the blacks. Hostile natives are an accepted risk of the game that will trouble very few of you. You have, now, so many things in your favour: railways, roads, quick and easy transport almost everywhere, easily got food supplies, comparatively little physical hardship, modern methods of working—you have even "new chum's luck" on your side. In the history of almost every mineral field in Australia, New Zealand, and Tasmania, new chums have stumbled on many of the rich claims. For instance: on the rich Edie goldfield recently found in the Mandated Territory of New Guinea, the richest claim was pegged by a new chum digger. He pitched his camp on it and didn't know the gold was there until months afterwards. The big £6000 odd nugget found in Westralia a week or two ago was picked up by a seventeen year old lad. You can go right back to the very beginning of gold-mining in Australia and prove for yourself that new chum diggers have their share of luck. So go out with confidence. Even if you go to an old field you have your luck backed up by your water knowledge, and that knowledge if you can apply it will bring you success.

Go out determined that you will "strike" something; determined to learn all you can as you go along; and you will find prospecting a fascinating game. You will like it better than you liked "hide and seek" as a youngster. "Nature hides her secrets well." But those who search carefully, those who have the eyes to see and the head to reason, will find. No man can say that your pick is not the one that is going to open up a new goldfield. If you do that you will not only make your fortune, but may prove yourself Australia's greatest friend in her time of need.

I have written this book in the hope that you will find a new goldfield. Do that and I shall be the gainer for one of my army of prospectors will have saved Australia. We will be proud men indeed.

THE BEST OF LUCK

June 1946. The above was written in 1931. In succeeding years Tennant's Creek goldfield in Central Australia was discovered, and Portland Roads in Cape York Peninsula. There were also smaller finds in various areas of the continent.

XXIX

The Cyanide Process

You must have a working knowledge of a few chemicals for this. To explain the process in detail would take a number of chapters. It is used for the recovery of gold which has escaped in the tailings, gold from complex ores as a rule. The process extracts gold and silver from the ores, by dissolving the precious metals. The gold is then precipitated by charcoal or zinc shavings. Ordinary "free ores" are easy of cyanidation, but, when the ores are complex (that is, containing mixed minerals), the process becomes so "complex" that you must have experience and a knowledge of chemicals to help you out. You must learn to make up your solutions, the strength of those solutions, and the strength and quantity of solution needed to dissolve the particular percentage of gold in your sands.

Probably a future edition of this book will be considerably enlarged to give you a practical plant and working process in detail. At present, here is a condensed but thorough working description for the man who knows just a smattering of the process. The far-flung experience of a number of Mines Department men has gone into this description under ordinary "working miner" conditions, and so, if you are thinking of cyaniding old tailings or dumps, or your own crushed ore, here it is. The information given below was supplied by the Department of Mines, New South Wales. I advise you to study well the last three lines, marked "Essentials."

By the way, should you seriously think you have something worthy of putting through the cyanide,

I know the Department mentioned would give you the benefit of the advice of some pretty good men.

****

SMALL SCALE SAND CYANIDATION
PRACTICAL NOTES

These notes are expressly compiled for the working operator desirous of treating small tonnages of gold-bearing material by cyanidation. The material will consist of residual sand or a mixture of sand and slime. If the product does not come within this category it would be necessary to get further advice covering fie particular dump in question.

In considering a proposition for cyanidation, it is first necessary to determine the contained gold value and tonnage. The quantity of gold necessary to make the venture payable will depend largely upon local conditions, while the tonnage will determine the amount that can be spent on plant. After the gold values have been obtained and found satisfactory, it is then necessary to find out how much can be extracted by cyanidation. In some cases the material is refractory and may not yield itself to cyanide treatment. However the test will decide the point, also the amount of cyanide and other chemicals required. With the assurance that sufficient gold can be obtained by cyanidation to make the venture successful and the tonnage is sufficient to justify the erection of the plant, the foundation is laid for a successful operation.

For the material mentioned the treatment will consist of leaching in vats. These are constructed of stout galvanized iron and tarred throughout. The filter bottom can be made by spacing brick bats about one inch apart. These are covered with hessian or bags on which is placed a three-inch layer of coarse sand. The sand charge is placed on top of this. A vat twelve feet x three feet gives a handy sized charge. The vat is fitted with the necessary pipe fittings, one to lead the cyanide solution on to the vat, the other to drain the gold-bearing solution to the zinc box for precipitation.

When charging the vat the requisite amount of lime is mixed throughout. The cyanide solution charge can be made up in a separate tank or the required amount of cyanide dissolved under the charge tap of the vat. About 3 lb. of cyanide to each ton of water gives a good working charge. After standing overnight the first cyanide solution charge is drawn off through the zinc box. The return solution from the zinc box is run through the vats till ready

162

for discharging (about seven days). Should sand and slime have to be treated it is necessary to have them as dry as possible before cyaniding. The mixture should be about 1:1. Care must be taken not to unduly pack this charge otherwise difficulty will be experienced in getting solution through the charge.

Precipitation of the gold is effected on zinc shavings. Sometimes the addition of a small quantity of lead acetate is helpful to this operation. Clean up is done by washing the zinc over a 1/4-inch mesh screen. What goes through is acided with sulphuric acid, and the residue dried and smelted with borax and a little sand.

For testing the cyanide solutions, a 10 ccm. pipette and 50 ccm. burette is necessary. Silver nitrate solution can be purchased of such strength that 1 ccm. equals 0.1 per cent potassium cyanide, taking 10 ccm. for the test. It is essential to know that you have free cyanide in the solution leaving the leaching vat. This ensures maximum gold extraction and successful gold precipitation on the zinc shavings.

ESSENTIALS

1. Ascertain that there is sufficient gold to pay.
2. That the solution leaving the vat has free cyanide.
3. Regular assays for guidance.

Cyaniding for Gold explains the process in detail.

XXX

Prospecting for Oil

I am greatly honoured by Mr Idriess in being asked to contribute to the fourth edition of his *Prospecting for Gold* a chapter on prospecting for oil. In these hard times every prospector is on the look out for anything which will give him a hope of making a living, and the search for oil comes in for a fair share of attention. Unfortunately there is a great deal of misconception as to oil and its mode of occurrence, and, as a result, there is much misplaced energy and a good deal of disappointment, both unnecessary if a few of the main principles of the subject are understood.

There are some widespread popular fallacies with regard to the possibilities of obtaining oil in Australia, such as the ideas that "Australia is too old," that there is no oil south of the equator, that oil is met with only in the tropics, and so on. Space does not permit of dealing with these beliefs in detail, but all are without a shadow of foundation. There is no good reason why oil should not be found in payable quantities in Australia, and the writer believes that it will be found so soon as the incorrect methods employed in the past give place to better ones, applied with sufficient energy.

Unfortunately, while the search for gold can be commended to the individual prospector, possessed of little more than a pair of strong arms, and a reasonable amount of common sense, the same cannot be said of the search for oil. In the case of gold, it is gold that has to be looked for. In the case of oil, on the other hand, it is only in the rarest instances that any actual oil is discovered by the prospector. This is particularly the case amongst the older geological formations, including those in which oil is "likely" in Australia. The search for oil resolves itself (or should undoubtedly resolve itself), in the earliest stages, into a geological survey which calls for very detailed training in the science of geology.

Among the more disturbed members of "young" geological formations, like those met with very widely in California, Persia, the East Indies and elsewhere, the occurrence of "seepages" of oil is not infrequent. Such seepages, in formations of this kind, have been responsible for the discovery of oilfields. Seepages, however, are relatively extremely uncommon in oilfields in older geological formations; and in places where even young formations are not very much disturbed, geologically speaking. In Australia itself the widespread younger geological formations are not disturbed in this way. Hence the occurrence of such indications as "seepages," "gas-blows," "mud-volcanoes" and the like, cannot be looked for.

It is an unfortunate fact that there exist quite a number of other appearances which are superficially very like oil seepages and gas blows; and these give rise to false hopes and ultimate disappointment.

Everyone, in these days of motor transport, is familiar with the appearance of films of oil on water. Such films take the form of smears which are either grey or show rainbow colours. Consequently, many people who see similar grey or rainbow colours on natural waters leap to the conclusion that they are formed by oil.

Any thin film of transparent material will produce such colours, owing to the breaking up of the colours of the sunlight. A soap bubble is an example of this. Under natural conditions, where water contains any iron in solution, the formation of a thin film of iron oxide (rust) is extremely common. This causes prismatic colours somewhat closely resembling those due to oil. The two films can be distinguished by stirring up the water. An oil film will curl into spirals: an iron film will break into spangles. Further, there is often a good deal of rusty looking mud on the bottom of pools containing iron waters, and pools into which gum leaves have fallen tend to become inky looking. Such waters, too, tend to make tea black and inky. This is by far the commonest of the mistaken "signs" of oil. It is so extremely unlikely that true oil seepages will be met with under the geological conditions existing anywhere in Australia that the first enquiry on finding a real oil scum should be, "Who put it there?" There are people about who do not hesitate to "fake" oil showings, just as there are people who are not above "salting" a gold prospect.

If what appears to be a genuine oil seepage is discovered, the first thing to do is to collect enough of the material for analysis (not less than four ounces if possible), and send it to the nearest Mines Department for testing.

Even the discovery of genuine oily material does not mean an oilfield. The intrusion of volcanic rock into strata containing even small amounts of coaly matter is likely to produce tarry and oily substances by distillation. These may be met with in small quantities, even in the volcanic rocks themselves, as is the case in the Macpherson Range.

Spontaneous combustion of coal produces a like result. Quite extensive "oil prospects" were described in Alaska, which were shown to be due to this action. Nearer home, spontaneous combustion of coal in the material of a railway embankment in New South Wales has produced a tarry and oily substance which has been mistaken for oil, even by somewhat experienced analysts.

Petroleum is nearly always associated with more or less natural gas; but the reverse is not true. Natural gas occurs very commonly in cases where no oil is present. Such natural gas forms very readily whenever vegetable matter, either recent or fossil, is undergoing decomposition. Any swamp will give considerable quantities of marsh gas if the silt at the bottom is stirred up. This gas burns readily, and, if mixed with air in the right proportions, will explode violently. It is identical with the "fire damp" of a coal mine, which is formed by the slow decomposition of the coal. The coal does not need to be in definite "seams," but may be in the rocks in the form of small amounts of coaly matter, too insignificant to be noticed by a casual observer.

The many inlets round the Australian coast, which have been filled with silt and sand, produce such natural gases in large amounts; and numberless "discoveries of oilfields" have been made in consequence. There may be quite violent outbursts of gas occasionally. Such have been described in the formation of "mud islands" at the mouth of the Mississippi River. The writer has suggested a similar explanation for "eruptions" on a much smaller scale in the Gippsland Lakes.

If natural gas is met with under conditions suggesting that it may be associated with oil, it is important that a sample should be obtained for analysis. If it is bubbling through water it may be collected as follows. Take a large, wide-mouthed bottle, of not less than a quart capacity, and preferably larger.

A fruit preserving jar with a rubber ring as a seal is about the best receptacle ordinarily obtainable. Remove the cover and completely fill the bottle with water. Keeping the mouth entirely under water, turn the bottle upside down. If even the smallest trace of an air bubble is left in the bottle, start afresh. If not, bring the inverted bottle over the stream of gas-bubbles and allow the gas to displace the water until the bottle is nearly filled with gas. If the gas comes from several different points near together, collection may be assisted by the use of a wide funnel, such as an inverted tin dish with a hole in the bottom, placed so as to catch the discharge from as many of the "jets" as possible.

When the bottle is nearly, but not quite full, still keeping it upside down and under water, put on the top and close it down securely. Keep the bottle upside down, so that the water will form a gas-tight seal even if the rubber ring is faulty. The slightest contamination with air is to be avoided. Send the bottle, with strict instructions that it should not be up-ended, to the Mines Department for analysis. Gases from oil generally contain constituents which can be recognized by the analyst. It must be remembered, however, that gases formed by the natural or artificial distillation of coal may contain exactly similar compounds. Much fruitless effort has been expended in consequence.

If the gas to be collected is not bubbling through water naturally, a pipe has to be fixed in some way so as to lead it through water in a tub; then the collection may be carried out as above described, allowing sufficient time for the air originally in the pipe to be replaced by the natural gas.

Certain kinds of waxy looking substances are sometimes mistaken for oil products. Even fine clay which feels and looks waxy on a freshly cut surface, is not infrequently mistaken for oil. One substance which is constantly being sent in for analysis as "bitumen" is formed from the droppings of marsupials in caves and under ledges. Owing to the action of microbes, the original droppings are altered, and a material is formed which will move like thick pitch, will run for quite considerable distances through cracks in the rocks, and which will burn with a bright flame. Naturally enough the average bushman thinks he has struck oil. This substance, however, will dissolve in water and make water brown, which true bitumen or oil will not do. It is full of phosphates which can be recognized by chemical tests.

All along the southern coasts of Australia and New Zealand, and sometimes at some distance inland from the shore, masses of real bitumen are met with. This is washed ashore and probably comes originally from the Antarctic. Similar material is met with on the shores of Chile, so that it can scarcely have a local origin, as is stoutly claimed by some people. Sometimes this material is soft and will float on sea water. When it has been exposed to the sun for any length of time it becomes darker, harder and heavier. In many instances it has been melted by the sun's heat and has flowed into cracks in the rocks, or has become mixed with the sand in such a way as to appear to have been formed locally. Many prospectors find it very difficult to accept its accidental origin; but there is little doubt as to this. This bitumen is by no means evenly distributed along our coasts, but tends to occur abundantly at certain places and to be much more scarce at others. This irregularity is not due, as is often stated, to local origin of the material, but to peculiarities in the "set" of the ocean currents. "Prospects" founded on the discovery of such bitumen, even in quite unlikely looking places, are certain to result in disappointment.

Real oil, wax and fat are sometimes met with under the most surprising circumstances. Samples of refined paraffin have been submitted for testing, derived from our beaches. Bees-wax is not at all uncommon. Even in the United States such false alarms are not unknown. I was told of one instance in which the genuine discovery of an oil "seepage" was ultimately traced to a "cache" of bacon buried by some long forgotten backwoodsman! It is necessary therefore to eliminate all the possible elements of chance before deciding that even a definite discovery of oil is the real thing. A golden rule is to collect as much as possible of the material for analysis, send it to the Mines Department, and, last but not least, accept the finding of the analyst.

Still another very frequent source of disappointment is "a smell of kerosene" in the rocks, clay, or water. Tests of materials, submitted to analysis in the belief that they contain oil, suggest that the sense of smell varies greatly in different people, and that most individuals can make themselves believe nearly anything they like. Any nasty smell is put down as "kerosene." In most instances it turns out to be more or less pure sulphuretted hydrogen (rotten-egg gas) derived from the decomposition of organic matter.

One very frequently hears that "horses will not drink this water now as they used to do," the suggestion being that, for some entirely unknown reason, natural oil, which must have existed for thousands of years if it exists it exists at all in a given locality, has made itself apparent. The reason why horses turn up their noses at water in certain places is because the water in question becomes inoculated with microscopic plant life of certain kinds, rendering it unpalatable. Further, certain types of such plants actually produce natural oils, which may accumulate in sufficient quantities to be capable of detection, as oil, in the mud and silt at the bottom. This fact of actual development of oily organic products from living plants and animals must be remembered. The "Coorongite" of South Australia is an example.

The kind of real oil indication most likely to be encountered by the ordinary prospector in Australia is what is known as "tar sand." A bed of sandstone which is saturated with oil at a depth, may show quite remarkable features where it comes to the surface. Oil, leaking slowly through it, becomes "perished" in contact with the air, and becomes converted into a dark substance, so that a freshly broken surface of the rock may look like a piece of broken asphalt pavement. The discovery of such a tar sand would be of the utmost importance.

The testing of supposed oil showings by amateurs cannot be recommended, as there are so many pitfalls, and "a little knowledge is a dangerous thing." If the prospector is nevertheless anxious to try his hand, a chloroform test is quite easy to carry out, though often difficult to interpret aright. Place some of the suspected material in a small *thoroughly clean* bottle, with a little chloroform. Close the bottle with a *clean* cork, and shake it for about a minute. Do not allow the chloroform to stand long on the material, as substances other than petroleum dissolve gradually in it. Allow the sand and clay to settle, and gently pour the clear chloroform into a *clean* saucer. Allow this to stand in a draught, but keep flame of any kind away, as the chloroform is very inflammable. If appreciable oil is present it will leave an oily scum on the saucer. It is well to make a "blank" test with an equal quantity of the chloroform, as many samples of the latter leave an appreciable residue on evaporation. The *cleanliness* above insisted on does not mean ordinary "wash up" cleanliness, but freedom from any oily residue. This is best obtained, after ordinary washing, by rinsing with a couple of lots of chloroform.

As has been indicated, this test cannot be recommended to prospectors, as there are many pitfalls in its application, and confusion and disappointment are likely to result. Perhaps the best advice which can be given is as follows. Observe anything which may suggest the presence of oil. Suspect foul play and ask yourself, "Who put it there, and what had he to gain by doing so?" Remove all traces from the surface and from immediately below the surface. Stand over the spot with a shot-gun to guard against further attempts at "salting." If you are satisfied that the material appears again under natural conditions, collect it carefully, and send it to a Mines Department for investigation. As pointed out above, it is considered exceedingly improbable that surface indications of oil will be met with in Australia, though they are much more likely in New Zealand and New Guinea.

The true indication of the possibility of existence of an oilfield is afforded by the geological structure of an area, and not necessarily by any actual oil indications at the surface. There are, perhaps unfortunately, many popular and semi-popular works on oil geology on the market. The trouble is that oil geology is by no means the simplest aspect of the subject, and "a little knowledge is a dangerous thing" in this case also. To a man who does not possess a fair grounding in general principles, the descriptions in such works convey impressions founded on ordinary experience, and such impressions are apt to be very wide of the mark. The writer has, officially, made a number of enemies by being compelled to point out that, contrary to the belief of his correspondents, the descriptions in such textbooks are not written in plain English, but that a certain amount of geological knowledge is presupposed, and the descriptions are really technical in character.

While there are hundreds of oilfields possessing structures other than "anticlinal" and even devoid of any trace of surface structure at all, the commonest type of structure, and the one which should be looked for in the preliminary stages of exploration in any "new" district, is some form of bending or arching of the strata. When layers of stratified rock, originally deposited as horizontal beds of sediment, are bent so that they form a trough, the resulting structure is called a "syncline"; when the result is an arch, the structure is called an "anticline." When the "axis of the anticline" which corresponds with the ridge pole of a roof, is itself bent upwards in the middle, the anticline becomes a "dome." The reader will say, "This is all simple; in plain English a syncline is a valley and an anticline is a ridge: why use Greek names for them?" This is just where the mistake comes in. The foldings of the rocks which have produced the anticlines, synclines and domes took place millions of years ago. The hills and valleys, of today are mere things of yesterday, and have little or no relation to the foldings. Hills are not anticlines in the majority of instances, and present day landscape features can be connected with geological structure only after very long and careful geological survey. Anticlines and synclines refer to underground rock structures and not to surface hills and valleys. Hence it is that the search for oil demands a large amount of geological experience.

Foldings in the rocks are determined by the geologist by measuring the "dips" or slopes shown by the individual beds in the formations and by applying geometrical constructions to the information so obtained. Only after such work has been done, and done very thoroughly, can it be determined whether or not an anticline or dome is present. As repeatedly stated above, such work cannot be recommended to the amateur geologist, but calls for much professional training of a high order.

In referring to such structural features it must be repeated that there are hundreds of oilfields in which no anticlinal structure has been discovered; but there are thousands in which this structure is recognizable. Scores of oilfields have been discovered accidentally or by blind stabbing. Such "searching for a needle in a haystack" is more or less justified in a region in which oil is known to be abundant. In such regions there is always a sporting chance of success. In a continent in which, as yet, no considerable oilfields have been located, it is surely obvious that the search in any but the most likely places is rank waste of time and money. Even in the most likely places the risks of failure are very high: in blind stabbing they are enormous. One of the commonest claims put forward by some of the so-called oil experts is that "this country is exactly like such and such an oilfield in California." Such a statement should be sufficient to condemn the man who makes it without further consideration. In the first place, there is no place in Australia where the geological structure approximates to that in California, and no close analogy is possible so far as the fundamentals of oil occurrence are concerned. In the second place, the presence or absence of oil, thousands of feet underground, can have no influence upon the growth of vegetation on the surface soil. In the third place, be it in California or Mexico or in any other oil producing country, oil is found under the most varied of surface conditions. It occurs on mountain tops, in deep valleys, on plains and under seas and lakes. Some of the richest fields are amongst the orange groves of California; others in the midst of salty deserts. There is *no type of country*, indicated by climatic or topographic conditions which is, more than another, "typical oil country."

This does not mean that there are no indications which may serve as guides or cautions in the search for oil. Though we do not know conclusively just how oil is produced in nature, it is certain that it can occur only in certain types of formation, and that other types of formation can be ruled out of court, except for minor and accidental freak occurrences which are easily explained in the neighbourhood of actual oilfields.

In the first place oil is a volatile substance which can easily be destroyed or evaporated by heat. Hence it is useless to look for it in those rocks which have been subjected to great heat and pressure during or subsequent to their formation. This rules out, immediately, all rocks which were at one time melted, like granite, diorite and volcanic rocks. It rules out, also, all the older sediments which have been altered into slate, schist and similar rocks by heat and pressure. The experienced prospector will recognize immediately that this cuts out entirely the whole of those rocks amongst which he may reasonably look for gold and other metals. It is not too much to say that if there is the slightest chance of metalliferous reefs, oil can be neglected.

This leaves only those formations built up of sediments, which have not been altered by heat or pressure, but which are still in the form of unaltered sandstone, shale, conglomerate, limestone and the like. Not all of these are equally favourable. While the statement is subject to modification and cannot be accepted as the belief of all competent oil geologists, the bulk of present day opinion is unfavourable to rocks formed under freshwater conditions, as mother rocks for oil. It is precisely in such rocks that coal seams and kerosene shale are developed; and it is more than probable that these substances represent accumulations of organic material, which, if they had been developed under other sets of conditions, might have formed oil. Hence the presence of coal or kerosene shale is unfavourable for oil in the *immediate* vicinity.

Marine sediments, in which fossils of sea animals of various kinds may be found by patient search, are, on the whole, the most favourable types of formation in which to look for oil. It must be remembered, however, that past changes in sea level have resulted in freshwater and marine sediments being sandwiched in together in very close proximity to one another. Unless, however, some suggestion of the existence of marine conditions can be recognized, a thick series of freshwater beds must be regarded with suspicion.

This limitation applies only to the rocks as the actual original source of the oil. Since oil is a liquid, it is capable of migrating for considerable distances through the pores of rocks which are not too close in texture. In these circumstances it is possible for oil *reservoirs* to be formed in rocks which are, of themselves, unfavourable for oil *production*.

The degree of folding favourable for oil concentration, to which the rocks may have been subjected, varies with their age. In formations as old as or older than the chief coal bearing formations of Australia, anything like acute folding, producing dips (inclination of strata) greater than about 20 degrees from the horizontal, are open to suspicion. On the other hand, in very young rocks, like those of California, there is little accumulation of oil in structures in which the bending is not fairly pronounced. Rocks of this age in Australia are generally practically without folding, and hence, though otherwise favourable, are unlikely to contain much oil in fold structures. Structures of other types, too complicated to explain in a book of this kind, and unrecognizable by the untrained observer, may be oil bearing; but the horizontal Tertiary formations of Australia cannot be recommended to the attention of the "prospector." In New Guinea, Papua and New Zealand, younger rocks of the Californian type, sharply folded, considerably broken and capable of producing seepages and other surface indications of oil, are widespread.

In conclusion, the advice to the prospector in Australia in connection with the search for oil may be summed up as follows:—In country "likely" for reef gold and other metals, do not bother your head about oil. In regions of sedimentary sandstone, shale and limestone, pay particular attention to the lay of the strata. If the individual bands slope steeply, as a general rule the indication is bad (except in parts of New Guinea, Papua and New Zealand). If the slopes of the individual layers are gentle, lay them down on a map as accurately as possible, indicating the down grade direction by an arrow. When a number of such arrows have been inserted, examine the map, and pay special attention to places where the arrows point away from one another in a pretty regular and conspicuous fashion. There are certain appearances, such as those known to geologists as "cleavage," "current bedding," etc., which are almost certain to be mistaken for "dip" by an inexperienced observer, but such mistakes will become apparent when the map is critically examined by a geologist. At such points anticlinal structures may be developed; but do not confuse hills and valleys with anticlines and synclines respectively. If anticlinal structures are suspected, in rocks of suitable character, report the fact to the Mines Department and have it investigated. A few typical photographs help very materially.

Keep a sharp lookout for fossils, particularly sea shells, corals, etc. Do not neglect the smaller forms. Many beautiful fossils, no larger than a pin's head, may be present, and often these tiny forms are of much greater importance, from the oil aspect, than are the big shells. In collecting fossils it is not sufficient to get them and put them in a pocket, all together, possibly sorting them out from memory hours, days, or weeks later. Each individual piece must be wrapped, on the spot, in a separate piece of paper, and labelled with the exact locality. If two or more pieces are wrapped together, the result is certain, they will chafe through the paper and be lost. It is not sufficient to indicate the general area from which the fossil came. The locality must be indicated, preferably in terms of direction and distance from some definite landmark, in such a way that the exact spot can be located from the description. Send a selected collection of the fossils to your Mines Department for investigation.

Except in New Guinea, Papua and New Zealand, view every suggestion of surface indications of oil with the utmost suspicion. Anticipate and investigate the probability of the indications having been "faked" by some evil minded person, probably for his own benefit. If, after all precautions have been taken, the "seepage" appears to be genuine, collect samples and submit them for official investigation.

Above all, bear in mind the fact that Government officials are just as anxious that oil should be found in Australia as are private individuals, and that they will not unnecessarily discourage anyone who has real indications to submit.

XXXI

Your Far Greater Chance

This book was written during the Depression years, the first edition appearing in 1931. Other editions were soon called for, and a few more chapters were added. It is now 1946, perhaps the most momentous year in mankind's history. Despite the terrible tragedy of the Great World War, this book has been in demand, and more editions would have been printed but for the shortage of man-power and paper. This sustained demand augurs well for those who decide to seek minerals now peace has come. For the demand for all minerals and mineral substances will be vast indeed, especially the demand for the base metals and numbers of the mineral earths.

Australia has produced a great quantity of gold since the first edition of this book was printed. From the doldrums, a new era in our mining history had been born, and it was firmly established when war broke out. At least two new fields of a good size had been found, one at Portland Roads in Cape York Peninsula, near Weymouth Bay, not far from the Batavia River diggings. So you see that even in country travelled over by prospectors whose lifetime is given up to mining, a field may be missed for years, even many years.

The other field, a large reefing field, was discovered under different, yet in one respect similar, circumstances, very heartening to those who have not had much prospecting experience. The prospectors responsible for the discovery were Henry James Udall and his wife—fine types, these two, deserving every bit of luck coming to them— while a man who played a great part in starting the field was "Woody" Woodruffe, telegraphist at Tennant's Creek Telegraph Station, a bushman with very little mining experience. At Tennant's Creek there were no diggings fairly handy, as at far away Portland Roads; there was just the isolation of Centralia. For all that, throughout the years an occasional wandering prospector had sunk a pot-hole here and there in the barren iron hills about seven miles distant from the lonely telegraph station.

For years something about these grim red hills had attracted the few prospectors in that harsh country of distances. Little wonder they failed to find the gold; it was not "supposed" to occur in such country, anyway. Also, it occurred under circumstances rarely found elsewhere. So for years at a time the lonely hills would be quite abandoned.

Then came Udall and his wife, battling their way through the Centre, fascinated by those harsh red hills. One day Mrs Udall picked up a stone on an old dump. She broke it. Gold was visible! Picture the excitement of those two, alone under the blazing sun of the Centre. This was the discovery of the Great Northern.

Now let "Woody" Woodruffe tell how he located his find; his story should be of interest to the inexperienced. "I felt certain there must be gold in those hills, Jack, but I knew very little about the game. So I wrote to Adelaide for a prospecting book, read it up, and started pottering about the hills when off duty. I began to get a few colours—which made me keener. One day I sent two niggers out with a bag and promised them tobacco if they'd bring me in a sample of every unusual stone they could find. One of those stones, when I dollied it, showed a decent tail of gold. I loamed where the niggers picked up the stone and got a tail of gold that made my heart go pit-a-pat. But I had to attend to my duties, and the station was seven miles away. So I got Jack Nobel to costean it for me. This proved the cap of a reef but not the reef itself. I wrote to old prospector Garnet if he'd come along and give the show a go. He did, and found the reef. We pottered about a bit more and struck the gold. And that's how we found the "Peter Pan.""

Tennant's Creek since then, of course, has developed into a big field.

In various areas of the continent smaller finds have been made, while very considerable quantities of gold have been won from old fields and the re-treatment of old dumps and tailings. But the war put a stop to what had grown into a prosperous gold-mining industry.

But now you will have the chance of starting out in a mining industry of vastly greater opportunities—opportunities already known and opportunities as yet undreamed of—than awaited the men who went looking for gold during that heart-breaking Depression. It was only gold that was of much use to them, but now the world wants a hundred minerals and mineral substances, so your opportunities are a hundredfold greater than at any time in the last twelve years. The production value of many base minerals will be far, far greater than that of gold, great as this will be.

Apart from the demand for base minerals, quite a new factor has recently entered the world's commercial life, and this will have a tremendous effect upon the mining and many other industries. The discoveries of what we may loosely call "chemical mining", of the synthetic and plastic industries, and also the development of industries new to Australia, have created an ever-growing demand for raw materials. And numbers of these, and increasingly so, will come from the Mineral Kingdom.

Merely, as an instance of how an entirely new industry can create a demand for minerals, glance at Australia's highly successful optical glass industry. Among the raw materials required are sand containing not less than .02 per cent of iron, a particular grade of lime, soda, lead-oxide, and barium-oxide, as well as a particular grade of fire-clay for the melting pots. So that, in unexpected ways a rising tide of new industries and developments will soon bring an increasing demand for mineral products previously thought to be of little or no value. And it is the prospectors and miners who must find and produce these materials.

Yet another demand for minerals will be as metals in alloys. Many "artificial" metals are now made, and these must first come from previously found and mined minerals. These alloys really are going to develop into a great industry. For instance, a particular mixture of copper, nickel, and aluminium, specially treated, can be made into a magnet that will lift one hundred times its own weight. Imagine how useful such magnets will be in the heavy industries. Again, from those same metals an alloy can be made so light that it will almost "float". It is easy to visualize a demand for vast quantities of such an alloy in the aeroplane and motor-car industries of the future. Your chance comes in prospecting for the bauxite and the clay deposits that contain aluminium, and for the copper and nickel deposits. If you could only find a decent-sized nickel deposit in Australia it would be worth more to you, and immeasurably more to the country, than a gold mine.

Yet again, recent scientific discoveries have taught and are teaching us how to synthesize metals for special purposes, "fixing" them so that they are capable of doing jobs they could not do in their natural state, and giving them all manner of new properties. As we advance in this metallurgical science, the needs of industry will create a terrific demand for many kinds of minerals, some of which may be quite strange to you.

These things give you all the more chances.

It would be easy to write a book of this size describing how and why minerals and mineral substances will now be in increasing demand, but this is only a note to remind you to keep your eyes open for other minerals as well as gold, tin, etc. You have many more chances ahead of you as mineral-hunters than as gold-seekers only. It is a big job, of course, to detect the presence of minerals you are not familiar with; it needs experience and some knowledge of the game, but if you have mastered this little book it will give you a good start, anyway. It will bring you up-to-date with the methods of seeking for and working gold, tin, opals, osmiridium, and platinum. And that is a jolly good start in the mining world. Get hold of a copy of *Fortunes in Minerals* if you can, the information there should help you quite a lot in the identification of many other minerals. The man with many strings to his bow has the greater chance of one arrow striking the bull's-eye. Just think about the one-shot rifle, and the many-shot tommy-gun.

So it will be with you. Learn all you can about all minerals and you will have many more chances.

Here is a list of minerals and mineral substances of value, just to give you an idea of the numerous valuable substances that the earth contains. And now—good luck to you.

Aluminium	Coal	Iridium	Scheelite
Antimony	Cobalt	Kaolin	Shale
Alunite	Copper	Lead	(mineral)
Arsenic	Dolomite	Limestone	Sulphur
Asbestos	Diamataceous	Magnesite	Talc
Barytes	Earths	Magnetite	Tellurium
Bauxite	Emery	Mica	Tantalite
Bismuth	Felspar	Manganese	Tin
Beryllium	Fluorspar	Molybdenite	Titanium
Carnotite	Fireclay	Monazite	Thoria
Chrome	Fuller's Earth	Nickel	Uranium
China Clay	Graphite	Ochres	Vanadium
Calcium	Gypsum	Osmium	Wolfram
Cinnabar	Iron	Rutile	Zinc
Cadmium	Iridsomine	Silver	Zirconium

GLOSSARY

Alluvial.—Clay, sand and gravel deposited by running water.

Amy.—A test of the mineral contained in a larger mass by extracting and weighing the product of a sample.

Auriferous.—Gold-bearing.

Basalt.—A greenish or brownish-black rock, igneous in origin, of compact texture and considerable hardness.

Bedrock.—The solid rock underlying all alluvial deposits.

Bismuth.—A hard, brittle metal of greyish-white colour, reddish tinged, used chiefly as an alloy.

Catchment area.—The entire area from which drainage is received by a reservoir, river, or the like.

Chain.—66 feet.

Colour.—A particle of gold which shows on washing alluvium in the pan or dish.

Concentrates.—The heavy residue of mineral left after washing pay dirt

Copper pyrites.—A sulphide of copper: a bright, crystallized, yellow, metallic-looking ore.

Crimping tool.—An apparatus which folds the edges of a cartridge case inward so as to close the mouth partly and confine the charge.

Cyanide process.—A process of gold extraction performed by passing an auriferous solution of potassium cyanide over zinc shavings, by which the values are precipitated.

Debris.—The loose fragments detached from the bedrock and washed down.

Diorite.—A granular, crystalline, igneous rock, commonly of soda-lime feldspar and hornblende, but often containing pyroxene or biotite, and sometimes quartz.

Driving.—Advancing horizontally by excavation, as a tunnel, gallery, level.

False bottom.—A stratum of barren alluvium, usually of fine grade, separating two layers of pay-dirt.

Flume.—An artificial channel for a water-course: an inclined channel, usually of wood and often supported on a trestle, for conveying water from a distance to be utilized for power, transportation, etc.

Friable.—Easily crumbled, pulverized, or reduced to powder.

Fulcrum.—The support, as a wedge-shaped piece, or a hinge, about which a lever turns.

Granite.—Crystalline rock composed of feldspar, quartz and mica.

"Grass roots."—A term used where a working is started from, or worked up to, the surface.

Head (of water).—The pressure resulting from the height of the source of water above the opening from which it issues.

Iron pyrites.—The commonest of the sulphides of iron, composed of pyrite and marcasite.

Lead.—An alluvial deposit in an old river-bed.

Levels, to take.—The operation of using an instrument to find a horizontal line, to ascertain the differences of level between points of the earth's surface.

Loam.—Clay, clayey earth, mud.

Loaming.—A method of prospecting for a metal-bearing vein or mineralized area in which dirt is washed from places chosen systematically around and up the slope of a hill. Presence, absence, and the number of colours in the dish eventually indicate the mineral source.

Mullocky.—Mullock is rock containing no gold, also, refuse from which gold has been extracted.

Osmiridium.—A native alloy of the metals iridium and osmium, usually occurring in flattened grains with platinum.

Paddock.—An excavation made in a flat away from a river.

Platinum.—A somewhat rare metal of a white colour like silver, but less bright, very heavy, ductile and malleable, unaffected by all simple acids, and fusible only at extremely high temperature.

Plumb-bob.—The bob, or weight, of a plumb-line, which is a line or cord, having at one end a weight (plumb-bob), usually of brass or lead, used to determine vertically.

Puddle.—To disintegrate the clay in pay-dirt before washing.

Puggy.—Moist, clammy.

Quartz.—A form of silica occurring in hexagonal crystals which are commonly colourless and transparent, but sometimes also yellow, brown, purple, green, and other colours. It is sometimes opaque.

Quartzite.—A metamorphosed sandstone. A rock containing usually about 98 per cent silica, with a small percentage of foreign materials, chiefly iron.

Race.—An artificial channel leading water to or from a point where its energy is utilized.

Rubble.—Loose angular stones or fragments of broken material forming the upper covering of some rocks, and found beneath alluvium or overlying soil; also, water-worn stones.

Scheelite.—Tungstate of calcium, found in brilliant crystals of various colours.

Shaft.—A pit sunk from the surface; an opening more or less perpendicular sunk on, or sunk to reach, the vein.

Shammy.—Chamois: a soft, pliable leather from sheep, goats, deer, etc.

Shingles.—Loose coarse alluvial material, worn off from solid bodies, having a majority of pebbles bigger than a walnut.

Slate.—A dense, fine-grained rock produced by the compression of clays, shales and certain other rocks, so as to develop a characteristic cleavage, which may lie at any angle with the bedding plane. It is commonly dull bluish or grey in colour.

Sludge.—Mud, mire, or ooze, covering the surface of the ground or forming a deposit at the bottom of rivers, etc.

Spit.—To dig with a spade.

Sump hole.—A shallow pit, dug at a conveniently low point in bedrock, into which is washed the spoil broken down by hydraulicing; in the sump hole is placed the gravel pump or jet elevator intake.

Tailings.—The refuse discharged from the tail or lower end of a sluice.

Tail-race.—The channel in which tailings, suspended in water, are conducted away.

Tamping.—Packing a blast-hole full of clay, etc., to get full force of explosion.

Tunnelling.—Excavating a passage underground, or through some body or substance.

Wash-dirt—Mineral-bearing sediment of streams and floods.

Wolfram.—A tungstate of iron and manganese, usually of a brownish or greyish black colour and submetallic lustre.

INDEX

Adam's River, 53

Air valve, 74

Alaska, oil in, 166

Alluvial gold. *See* Gold, alluvial.

Alluvial tin. *See* Tin, alluvial.

Amalgam, 37, 125-8, 131-3, 136-7, 139-142,

Amalgamation, 126-137

Anticlines, 171, 174

Antimony, 136, 139, 178

Arsenical pyrites, 70, 136

Baird, Bill, 159

Banjoing, 14-15

Basalt, 7, 92, 115, 155, 158

Batavia River, 158-9, 176

Battery, 111-120, 123-34, 140-2

Battery sites, cleaning up, 140-2

Beach sands, method of treating, 37

Bees-wax, 168

Bismuth, 115, 136, 178-9

Bitumen, 167-8

Black opal, 143-7

Blanket tables, 129

"Boil holes," 58-59

Boulders, to remove, 40-47, 87

Boxing, 20-26, 34 42-47, 98

Buhre's dry-blower, 104, 107

Bulolo River, 92

California, oil in, 165, 171-3

Cape York Peninsula, 108, 175

Carlson's dry-blower, 101-2

Cement wash, 86

Chile, 168

China Camp, 90

Chloroform test, 169

Chute, 118-19, 121

Claims, laws concerning, 48-9; pegging and registering of, 52-6, 145

Clay, blue slate, 52

Clay, treatment of, 18-9, 29,139

Clermont Goldfield, 100

Coal, spontaneous combustion of, 172-3

Complex ores, 135-7, 161

Concentrates, 11, 15, 18. 25-37, 59, 90, 99, 103, 126, 129

Conglomerate, 68, 86, 172

Coober Pedy, 143, 156

Cooktown tin-fields, 90

Coorongite, 169

Copper pyrites, 70, 179

Coramba, 123

Corduroy cloth, 126, 136

Cradling, 14-8, 26

Creeks, prospecting in, 6-59, 66-8, 109, 115, 118, 144

Crevicing, 9-10

Crucible, 133-41

Crushing, 112, 117, 120, 126, 128-137, 142

Cyanidation, 136, 161-2

Cyanide poisoning, 140

Cyanide process, beach sands, 161

Cyanide vats, 123, 136

Dam building, 34-9

Diorites, 87

Dish, for reef prospecting, 116-9

Dishing, 9-18, 25-37, 51-4, 103

Dolly-pot, 111-2, 117-9, 126

Dollying, 111-2, 120

Dry-blowing, 100

Dry-stacking, 61

Duck Creek, 155

Ebagoolah, 108

Edie Creek, 92

Elbows, 79

Electroplating of plates, 137

Elevator, 94-8

Emu Creek, 155

Equipment for prospectors, 5, 151

False bottom, 35, 48, 60, 180

Films, 165

Floaters, 116-7

Forking stones, 21, 32, 43, 89

Gas-blows, 165

Giant nozzle, 71-3, 77-8, 81

Gippsland Lakes, 166

Gira River, 53

Gold, alluvial, banjoing for, 14-9; boxing for, 20-4, 34-42; cleaning, 30-6; cleaning up, 23, 33, 59-63, 90, 98-103; cradling for, 18-24, 100; crevicing for, 8-11; dishing for, 9-18, 25; dry-blowing for, 100-110, 172; dry-stacking for, 61-5; equipment for mining, 5, 51; fine, cleaning-up of, 89, 100; how to distinguish, 14, 113, 119; likely localities for, 5-8; nuggets, 60, 108-110; pockets, 11-12; saving, 20-1, 30, 34-45, 63, 106-8, 128, 131, 136-7; secrets of, 51-60; sluicing for, box, 21, 31-3, 42, 87; sluicing for, hand, 21-34, 46-9, 60, 71-6, 87-98, 158; sluicing for, hydraulic, by gravitation, 70-9, 87; sluicing for, hydraulic, by machinery, 70-9; weighing, 179

Gold, new-chum, 15-21, 98, 159

Gold, reef, 111-5; chutes, 118; cleaning up, 30-6, 130, 140-2; crus

ing, 117, 120-30; equipment for mining, 5, 151; floaters, 116-7; indicators, 119; leaders, 111, 115, 118-20; likely localities for, 158; payable, 6-14, 25, 34, 51; specimens, 14, 58, 70, 111-19

Golden mica. Set Mica.

Granite, 9, 28, 42, 115, 172, 180

Granites, decomposed, 87

Grass roots, gold in, 66-7, 180

Gravitation, hydraulic sluicing by, 71-2, 91-3

Gullies, dry-stacking in, 61-4; nuggetty, 108; reef prospecting in, 111-17, 119-20 ; specimen, 117

Head-race, 84

Henderson, L., 123, 134

Hills, gold in, 8, 52, 112-18

Home Rule, 90

Hose, 71-3, 77-9, 81

Hydrant, 79

Hydraulic sluicing, by gravitation, 71-2; by machinery, 91-3

Indicators, 119

Iron, oxide of, 108, 165

Iron pyrites, no, 70, 136, 180

Iron sands, black, 29, 52, 54

Ironstone, 7, 9, 14, 52, 58, 67, 108-14, 119-20, 144, 155,

Kerosene, 137-39, 168, 172

Koroit, 155

Kyabra, 155

Lead, 178, 180-81

Leaders, 111, 115, 118-20

Leads, 11, 113, 115, 119

Levels, taking of, 64-5, 180

Light opal, 147, 150-56

Lightning Ridge, 55, 143

Loaming, 114, 180

Lode Hill, 87

Macpherson Range, 166

Magnifying glass, 7, 120

Mandated Territory of New Guinea, 21, 36, 92, 159

Mercury, 37, 112

Metals, "artificial", 177

Mica, golden, 70, 178

Miner's Right, 69-70

Mines Department, assistance given by, 5-6, 37, 64, 70, 113, 115, 121, 161, 166-70, 174

Mining laws, 69-70

Mississippi River, 166

Monitor. See Giant Nozzle.

Mount Amos, 90

Mount Finlayson, 90

Mount Romeo, 90

Mud-volcanoes, 165

Mundic, 70

"Mustard" gold, 39

Natural gas, 166-7

New Guinea. See Mandated Territory; Papua.

New Zealand, hydraulic sluicing in, 90, 97; oil in 95, 167, 170, 173-4

Nitrate of soda, 139

Nitric acid, 139

Northern Australia, dry-blowing in, 100

Nozzle, 71-3, 75, 77-9, 81, 84-6, 89-95, 106.

See also Giant Nozzle.

Nuggets, 108-110

Oil, in Australia, 166-73; in Alaska, 166; in California, 171-7; in New Guinea, 170, 173-4; in New Zealand, 170, 173-4; in Papua, 173-4

Oil reservoirs, 173

Opal, 55, 143-56

Opalton, 155

Osmiridium, 50-3, 178, 180

Otago Goldfields, 95

Overburden, removal of, 14, 28-32, 48. 57, 62, 68, 81, 86, 89-92

Paddocks, 12, 90

Papua, gold in, 21, 36, 53, 92; 278-oil in, 173; osmiridium in, 53-4

Paraffin, 168

Parvo, 155

Pestle, 112, 131

Peter Pan, the, 176

Pick, hammer-headed, 112

"Pin head" gold, 36, 42

Pipe-lines, 71-84, 90, 94-8

Pipeclay, 52

Pipes, hydraulic, home-made, 76-80

Plates, electroplating of, 137

Platinum, 46, 50-54

Pluto, 159

Plutoville, 159

Pockets, 11-12

Portland Roads, 160, 175

Potassium cyanide, 163, 179

Prospectors, equipment for, 5-7, 51

Prospector's reward claim, 70

Puddling, 18-9

Pug. See Clay.

Quartz, 7, 9, 14, 43, 52, 58, 67-8, 109-118, 125, 134-5, 180

Quartzite, 113, 181

Queensland, dry-blowing in, 100; hydraulic sluicing in, 101

Queensland opal fields, 154-5

Queensland Mines Department, 101

Quicksilver, 37, 122, 125-6, 129, 131-3, 136-9, 141

Quilpie, 155

Race, 23, 27-33, 47, 53, 61-5, 71-2, 84-90, 94-100, 125, 141; box-, 150; head-, 84; storm-, 63; tail-, 28, 32-3, 47-9, 182

Rankine's dry-blower, 103-4

Reef-mining, 111-15

Retorting, 132

Retorts, lining of, 141

Ripples, 15-18, 21, 25, 42-3, 98, 106, 137

River-beds, 5-6, 14, 104-8

Rivers, prospecting in, 50-68
Rossville, 90
Russell River, 92

Sample bag, 112
Samples, 112-120, 160, 168-9
Sands, 52, 98
Sandstone, 143-8
Scheelite, 178, 181
Screening, 69
Seepages, 165, 173
Serpentine country, 54
Shaft-sinking, 69
Sheet-iron, for pipes, 106, 131
Shipton's Flat, 90
"Shooting," 47
Silver, 18, 37
Slate, 8, 40-1, 80, 106, 139, 182
Sluice-box, 27-35, 43. 52-4. 62-8, 150-3
Sluicing, box, 26-35, 43, 45, 51-4, 62-8, 71, 150-3; hand, 36-50, 69-75. 79, 146, 156, 173; hydraulic, by gravitation, 112-58; hydraulic, by machinery, 146-7
Smelting, 133-4, 142
Sodium peroxide, 139
Solid ground, 55-60
South Africa, treatment of complex ores in, 136
South Australian Mines Department, 106
South Australian opal fields, 143
Specimen Country, 14
Specimen gullies, 117

Specimens, 14, 58-70, 111-19,
Spring dolly, 111, 117
Springsure, 155
Stamper, 117, 121-6, 128-9, 132-6, 141
Storm-race, 63
Storms, danger to sluicing claims from, 61
Streaming shovel, 99
Stuart Range, 143, 155
Sulphides, 136, 180
Sulphuretted hydrogen, 182
"Sump" hole, 94-5, 182
"Swirl holes," 57, 59
Synclines, 171, 174

Tail-race, 27-33, 47-9, 182
Tailings, 15-8, 26-31, 45-9, 55, 69, 92-5, 123-9, 136-7, 141, 161, 176, 182
Tar sand, 169
Tasmania, hydraulic sluicing in, 90; osmiridium in, 53
Tennant's Creek goldfield, 175-6
Thompson's Engineering and Pipe Co., Ltd, 94
Timber, to remove, 113
Tin, alluvial, 25, 56, 60, 66-8, 80-92, 95, 98, 142-4, 158, 178; new-chum, 98; reef, 115, 173
Tree-roots, gold in, 67
Trenching, 114-6
Tunnelling, 34, 69, 144, 182

Underground workings, 56

Wash, 7, 20, 24-5, 28, 31, 36-7, 43, 52-3, 57, 60-2, 67, 69, 86-7

Wash-stones, 9, 48, 52, 58, 62, 67-9, 89

Watercourses, gold in, 7, 66

Water power, 20-5, 46, 64

Water pressure, 72-4, 90

Water rights, 49, 69

Western Australia, dry-blowing in, 100

Wet season claims, 57, 61, 66

Wheel, 151-3

White Cliffs, 55, 144, 154

Windlass, 7, 68-9, 117, 144-5, 148, 156

ION IDRIESS

'Jack' Idriess was born in 1891 and served in the 5th Light Horse in the First World War. He returned to Australia to write The Desert Column, which was published following his huge success with Prospecting for Gold. He went on to write 56 books and was largely responsible for popularising Australian writing at a time when local publishing was still not considered viable. A small wiry mild-mannered man, Idriess was a wanderer and adventurer, with a vast pride in Australia, past, present and future.

ETT IMPRINT has been publishing Idriess for over 25 years, including:

Flynn of the Inland
The Desert Column
The Red Chief
Nemarluk
Horrie the Wog Dog
Prospecting for Gold
Drums of Mer
Madman's Island
The Yellow Joss
Forty Fathoms Deep
Lasseter's Last Ride
The Cattle King (audio)
Sniping
Shoot to Kill
Guerrilla Tactics
The Wild White Man of Badu
Gold Dust and Ashes
Headhunters of the Coral Sea

Lasseter's Diary

Transcribed with Mud-Maps

Harold Bell Lasseter had always claimed he had found an immense reef of gold hundreds of miles west of Alice Springs. In 1930, with Australia in the grip of Depression, a privately funded expedition led by Fred Blakeley, accompanied Lasseter in an attempt to relocate the reef. Blakeley left Lasseter at Ililba, and Lasseter continued his trek towards the Olgas with a dingo shooter and their camels. Lasseter continued to be introspective and brood, prompting Lasseter to go off alone with two camels.

In March 1931 an expedition led by bushman Bob Buck found Lasseter's body at Winter's Glen, and his diary at Hull's Creek, wherein it describes how after his camels bolted, he was alone in the desert, encountering a group of nomadic Aboriginals who offered offer him food and shelter. Blind, exhausted and dying, Lasseter made one last attempt to walk from Hull's Creek to Uluru.

The diary was purchased by Ion Idriess from Lasseter's widow in 1931, and from it he wrote the best-seller Lasseter's Last Ride. Here is the transcription of the diary with its original mud-maps and drawings.

GOLD-DUST AND ASHES

The Romantic Story of the New Guinea Goldfields

ION IDRIESS

The 26th illustrated edition now out from ETT Imprint, Exile Bay.

Brisbane Courier :-"His latest book is really the romance of the Edie Creek and Bulolo diggings, situated inland from Salamau; and with the discovery of the field are associated the names of diggers as "Shark Eye Bill" (William Park), Matt Crowe, Jim Preston, Arthur Dowling, Frank and Jim Pryke... men who in pre-war years, crept across the frontier, defying the Germans and dodging the head-hunters... These men endured terrible hardships, and frequently faced grim tragedy. Mr Idriess writes of it all, and writes of it as if he had been with them.. What a romance! What a story! It is packed with adventure, studded with splendid pen-pictures of pioneer prospectors, airmen, and patrol officers, and told with a fascinating simplicity that is borne from something very close to genius."

Milton Keynes UK
Ingram Content Group UK Ltd.
UKHW010857280324
440101UK00002B/321